"I was crazy about you— besotted.

"Oh, yes." Tane continued bitterly. "You were my whole world. How do you think I felt when I got home to find you'd disappeared? Until I met you, all I knew about love was how to live without it. You were sunshine in a cold, dark world, warmth that melted the grip of winter and made flowers bloom."

Laura, only too aware of how inadequate the words were, whispered, "I'm sorry, so sorry. I'd make it up to you if I could, but I..." Her voice trailed off at the glitter in his eyes.

"Oh, you'll make it up to me all right." A razor-sharp edge to his voice, he went on, "I promised myself that one day I'd find you and make you pay, and believe me, I shall enjoy every moment of it."

LEE WILKINSON lives with her husband in a three-hundred-year-old stone cottage in a Derbyshire village, which most winters gets cut off by snow. They both enjoy traveling and recently—joining forces with their daughter and son-in-law—spent a year going around the world "on a shoestring", while their son looked after Kelly, their much-loved German shepherd dog. Her hobbies are reading and gardening and holding impromptu barbecues for her long-suffering family and friends.

LEE WILKINSON

My Only Love

Harlequin Books

TORONTO • NEW YORK • LONDON
AMSTERDAM • PARIS • SYDNEY • HAMBURG
STOCKHOLM • ATHENS • TOKYO • MILAN
MADRID • WARSAW • BUDAPEST • AUCKLAND

ISBN 0-373-18603-7

MY ONLY LOVE

Copyright © 1992 by Lee Wilkinson.

First North American Publication 1995.

All rights reserved. Except for use in any review, the reproduction or utilization of this work in whole or in part in any form by any electronic, mechanical or other means, now known or hereafter invented, including xerography, photocopying and recording, or in any information storage or retrieval system, is forbidden without the written permission of the publisher, Harlequin Enterprises Limited, 225 Duncan Mill Road, Don Mills, Ontario, Canada M3B 3K9.

All characters in this book have no existence outside the imagination of the author and have no relation whatsoever to anyone bearing the same name or names. They are not even distantly inspired by any individual known or unknown to the author, and all incidents are pure invention.

This edition published by arrangement with Harlequin Enterprises B.V.

® and TM are trademarks of the publisher. Trademarks indicated with ® are registered in the United States Patent and Trademark Office, the Canadian Trade Marks Office and in other countries.

Printed in U.S.A.

CHAPTER ONE

WHEN the silver-haired old gentleman who had been browsing among the second-hand books for well over an hour finally went out without buying anything, Laura sighed, and from habit fingered the thin gold chain she wore around her neck.

Business had been slow for several months now and the new quarter's rent was due shortly. Worry about that, and where the money was coming from to pay Molly for taking care of Jamie, had fined down her heart-shaped face until the bones were prominent, and given her cornflower-blue eyes a shadowed look.

Glancing at the oval gold watch she wore on a plain black band, she found it was well past lunchtime. Normally she would have eaten a sandwich in the cramped, gloomy room at the back which served as living-room, bedroom, and kitchen. But today she had an urge to get out into the fresh air and sunshine, if only for a short while.

She felt restless and fidgety, almost certain that the short, balding man who had come in yesterday evening and bought a battered copy of *Ingoldsby Legends* had been Mr Jenkins.

Catching him looking at her with more than ordinary interest, she had kept her expression studiously blank. When she had handed him his purchase with an impersonal 'Thank you', to her relief he'd left without saying anything. All the same she had an uneasy feeling that he'd recognised her.

For over four years Laura had struggled to put the past behind her. Apart from those times when, out of the blue, memories had overtaken and swamped her, she'd been fairly successful. Or so she'd thought.

Now she wasn't so sure. If the sight of someone as innocuous as Peter Jenkins—if it *had* been Peter Jenkins—could unsettle her like this...

Five minutes later, her lunch in a fawn cotton tote bag, Laura had left the old Lulworth building and was walking briskly towards Central Road Park, which lay just around the corner.

A lively breeze lifted her shoulder-length ash-brown hair, flicked the points on the collar of her fawn and white striped shirtwaister, and flattened the skirt against her slim, bare legs.

Choosing a vacant bench overlooking the ornamental pond, she unwrapped a cheese sandwich. Before she had taken a single bite, a bright-eyed sparrow, his head cocked expectantly, was waiting by her sandalled feet.

As she broke off a piece of crust a shadow fell across the slatted bench. She glanced up at the tall, dark, broad-shouldered man who stood there, and the half-smile died from her lips.

Though his back was to the sun, his face thrown into shadow, it was just as she remembered it. As she would always remember it. Clean, powerful lines, thickly lashed eyes the blue-grey of wood-smoke, a mouth that was at once passionate and austere.

Strings of searing pain laced themselves tightly around Laura's heart, constricting it until she felt faint. There was a roaring in her ears and, although her eyes were wide open, a darkness all about her.

Gradually the roaring faded away, the darkness lifted, and the strings loosened enough to allow her heart to resume its beating.

'Hello, Laura.'

She remembered his clear, low-pitched voice. She would respond to that voice on her death-bed.

'Hello, Tane.' The greeting sounded so normal, so matter-of-fact, that she could hardly believe it was herself speaking. It was as if the years in between had never been.

'May I join you?' Without waiting for an answer, he sat down by her side and turned to look at her.

She had thought his face was exactly the same, but now she saw that it wasn't. It looked harder, tougher. There were lines etched on it that hadn't been there before, and the expression in his smoky eyes was a new one. They had always held warmth or amusement, tenderness or passion. Now... She shivered abruptly and looked away.

After a moment she asked huskily, 'How did you know where I was? You *did* know...?'

Tane nodded. 'I watched you come out of Belmont Books.'

'I suppose Peter Jenkins told you?'

'So you recognised him?'

'Yes.'

'He thought you might have. That's why I didn't let the grass grow under my feet.' Before she could begin to wonder what he meant, Tane added, 'It's been a long time, Laura.' The words were trite but there was a sudden bite to his tone, a resentment that matched the bitterness in his eyes.

Apprehension making her sound belligerent, she demanded, 'Why did you come to the shop? Why did you follow me here?'

'When Jenkins said he was almost certain it was you, I wanted to know, to see for myself.'

She gave him a hunted look. 'It would have been better to have left it. The past is over—dead.'

'The past is never dead,' he disagreed, as he had done once before. 'It's the past that makes us what we are today.'

Anger and hostility showed in the rigidity of his facial muscles, in the tenseness of his neck and shoulders, the whiteness of his knuckles.

Laura jumped to her feet with a quick, panicky movement. 'I . . . I have to be getting back.'

'Aren't you going to eat your lunch before you run?' There was a cruel little smile of satisfaction on his well-shaped lips which made it clear that it had been his intention to have her rattled, on the retreat.

Becoming aware that she was still clutching the sandwich, she said raggedly, 'I'm not very hungry,' and began to break it into pieces. They were immediately besieged by the ever-watchful sparrows and hungry pigeons, while a flotilla of ducks headed across the pond leaving V-shaped wakes in the water.

Grabbing her bag, Laura set off blindly, guessing, with a sense of doom, that he had no intention of letting her escape so easily.

A hand on her elbow brought her to a halt and swung her round. As her lips parted on an agitated protest, he said laconically, 'You're heading in the wrong direction.'

Her arm branded by his touch, unsure that her knees would continue to support her, she began to walk as fast as she could towards the park gates, desperate to get away from him.

'What have you been doing since you ran out on me?' Tane asked, easily keeping pace with her.

'I didn't run out on you.'

'Then what *would* you call it?'

She shook her head mutely.

'I call leaving without a word running out,' he pursued.

'If I'd stayed it wouldn't have worked,' she muttered desperately. 'We'd have ended up hating each other.'

'So what's new?'

Shaken to the core, she whispered, 'I don't hate you.'

'Perhaps I feel enough of that particular emotion for both of us.'

As her eyes widened in shock, he said, 'You didn't love me either. All the love was on my side. So maybe the depth of the second emotion is influenced by the depth of the first.'

'I *did* love you,' she choked.

'But not enough. You wanted to get married, but you didn't want to marry me on my terms.'

They had reached the shop and she fumbled in her bag for the key. She was turning it in the lock when he queried derisively, 'So what happened, Laura? Why haven't you married on *your* terms?'

Without pausing to think, she answered his taunt. 'I have.' Lifting her left hand, she displayed the plain gold ring on her third finger, and, as he stood as if turned to stone, closed the door in his face and pushed up the catch to lock it.

Somehow her wobbly legs carried her through the dark length of the shop and into the back room. She sank on to the nearest chair and covered her face with her hands.

He hated her. *Hated* her. His words burnt in her mind. 'Maybe the depth of the second emotion is influenced by the depth of the first... All the love was on my side'.

But it hadn't been. She had loved him fiercely, loved him with every atom of her being. From their very first meeting theirs had seemed a fairy-tale romance, starting with that most basic of ingredients, love at first sight. They had bumped into each other on a cold, wintry Monday in late February...

Laura had awakened that morning to find her small flat was in imminent danger of being flooded by a cracked pipe. Unable to find any way of turning off the water, she had decided to call David.

Only when his number was ringing out had she remembered that he would be on his way to Manchester, his firm having dispatched him there for a six weeks' computer programming course. With her bathroom already sloshing, she had spent half an hour trying to contact various plumbers. By the time she'd reached the imposing stone building, just off Piccadilly, which housed Carlson Holdings, she was more than ten minutes late for work.

It was a miserable day; a lazy wind cut through her too-thin mac and blew melting flakes of snow into her face. Head bent, she hurried up the stone steps and ran full tilt into a tall figure coming the other way.

The impact sent her reeling. She stumbled backwards down the steps and ended up in a heap on the wet pavement. Before she could begin to gather her scattered wits a man was crouching by her side, his face full of concern. 'I'm sorry. Are you hurt?'

She looked at the hard, clean-cut features, the thick peat-dark hair, the very masculine mouth that instantly made her own mouth yearn to touch it, and her heart did what felt like a series of back somersaults.

It was one of the most attractive faces she had ever seen. The eyes, like drifting wood-smoke between long, curly lashes, routed her completely. She stared into those fascinating eyes and was lost.

'Are you hurt?'

Becoming aware that he had repeated the anxious question, she said idiotically, 'I don't know,' adding breathlessly, 'In any case it was my own fault. I was in a hurry and not looking where I was going.'

'Well, let's see if there's any damage done before we start apportioning blame.'

Though subdued, controlled, there was an air of toughness and strength about him. He looked like a man who could smooth out the day-to-day problems of modern living with ease.

'You're not by any fortunate chance a plumber?' she asked as, with a large, well-shaped hand beneath her elbow, he helped her to her feet.

'Do you want a plumber?' he queried.

'Desperately.'

His blue-grey eyes gleamed with laughter. 'I could consider changing my occupation. Is it only plumbers who turn you on?'

'It's more a case of turning my water off.'

'Ah...'

'I can't find the stopcock and for all I know my flat may be awash. I've tried five different plumbers and all I can get are those idiotic answering machines.'

'Idiotic?'

She pulled a face. 'They don't *give* you an answer, they only take a message, so you don't know if you're going to get a plumber or——'

'Or five?'

'Exactly.'

'Yes, I see your problem.' He spoke gravely, but his eyes were devilishly amused.

'My only consolation is that my flat is on the ground floor so no one else should be affected.'

She was saying the first thing that came into her head, babbling like someone in a state of shock. A state of shock that had, she realised, little or nothing to do with her fall.

Unconsciously, she had been standing stork-like, favouring her left foot. Now, as she put her weight on it, she gave a gasp and lost colour at the swift shaft of pain.

He stooped and his long fingers moved gently but purposefully over her ankle, pressing and probing. 'I don't think anything's broken. It's probably a sprain. It's starting to swell already, so I suggest you go home and put your foot up, perhaps both feet if the water's getting deep, and wait for the plumber and the doctor.'

'Well, I don't know,' she said doubtfully. 'I don't want to take time off.'

'I can't see that you have a great deal of choice. Where do you work?'

'I'm in the general office, in the pool.'

'If that's so I'm sure they can spare you. What's your name?' he added briskly.

'Laura, Laura Peters.'

'Where do you live, Miss Peters?'

'Royal Mansions, Marylebone.' She responded to the casual note of authority in his voice without even thinking about it, and without her usual wry smile at the misleading poshness of the address.

He hailed a passing taxi, and before she had time to consider or argue he was half lifting her into it. Having given her address, he pushed a note into the driver's hand.

Embarrassed, she protested, 'No, really...I can pay my own fare. There's no need for you to——'

'It's the least I can do,' he said firmly. 'I was in a hurry myself and not taking proper care, so I'm certainly half to blame.' As the taxi drew away he smiled and sketched a salute.

Laura felt a sudden desolation, an absurd sense of loss, and had to tell herself forcefully not to be a fool.

David rang that evening, and when he heard of her mishap said how sorry he was to be away just when she needed him.

The flowers arrived the next day. A huge mixed bouquet, the most beautiful she'd ever seen, was delivered to her door. 'There doesn't seem to be a card with them,' the pimply youth informed her apologetically.

'It's quite all right,' Laura assured him. 'I know who they're from.' There was only one person who would send her flowers.

When David rang on Wednesday evening, she thanked him warmly.

'That was quick,' he remarked. 'Are they nice?'

'Absolutely gorgeous.'

'I just wish I could have brought them round myself. I'm missing you.'

'I'm missing you too,' she reciprocated, knowing it was what he wanted to hear.

The following lunchtime another bouquet, this time of carnations, narcissi and tulips, arrived. The youth handed her a small white envelope along with the flowers and remarked, 'He's remembered the card this time.'

It simply said, 'All my love, David'.

He really *was* missing her, Laura thought.

The sprain proved to be a fairly severe one and it was a full week before she was back at work.

Hobbling slightly, even in flat-heeled shoes, she climbed the fateful steps, the dark stranger's powerful face, with its squarish jaw and bitter-sweet mouth, clear in her inward eye. Laura had told herself repeatedly that she wouldn't think about him, and had then proceeded to do little else.

Having hung her coat in the staff cloakroom, she went through to the general office. Myra Gordon, who was in charge, gave her a distinctly cool look and informed her shortly, 'You're working upstairs in the "holy of holies".'

'I am?' Laura's surprise was evident.

'You were asked for personally.' There was a sourness to Myra's tone which left no doubt that *that* was the cause of her vexation. It went against current policy for one of her junior secretaries to be singled out for such an honour.

'Well, what are you waiting for?' she demanded tartly.

Laura said, 'I'm on my way,' and went. Speculating on which of the managers had asked for her, she took the lift up to the fourth floor. Looking attractively businesslike in her charcoal-grey suit and white blouse, her silky ash-brown hair taken up into a neat knot, she stepped out into the quiet, understated luxury of the top executive suite of offices.

In the foyer a smart brunette raised her eyes from her computer keyboard and queried, 'Miss Peters?'

'Yes.'

'Please go straight through.'

'Where will I be working?' Laura asked.

The girl gave her a curious look and said woodenly, 'In Mr Carlson's office. It's right down the corridor.'

At the end of a wide passage were two unmarked doors. Laura tapped on the nearest and opened it to find a large, opulently furnished boardroom. She was about to back out when a decisive male voice, a strangely familiar voice, called from the adjoining room, 'Good morning, Miss Peters. Please come through.'

As she obeyed, advancing across the thick pile of a mushroom-coloured carpet, a man appeared in the open doorway. Smiling a little at her startled face, he enquired, 'Did the plumber come?'

While her knees felt as if she'd been the recipient of a rugby tackle, she gaped at him. With the air of someone speaking to a not very bright child, he repeated the question.

'Yes, he came,' she managed. Then, swallowing, 'I was told I was working in Mr Carlson's office.'

'That's right,' he agreed casually, and repeated, 'Come through.' He moved aside and somehow her legs carried her into the adjacent room.

It was pleasantly light and informal, with two fine oak desks facing each other in front of the long windows. As Laura hovered by the nearest desk he came to stand quite close. He seemed taller, even more devastatingly attractive than she remembered.

'How is the sprain?'

She looked up at him. 'Mended, thank you.'

Almost inaudibly, he murmured, 'I kept telling myself that your eyes couldn't really be as blue as cornflowers. But they are.'

He appeared totally at ease in the handsome room, as if he *belonged*, but still she could hardly believe... The words coming out as practically a croak, she asked, 'Are you...?'

'Tane Carlson.'

Laura's soft mouth tightened as some of the implications struck her. 'You asked for me?' Even in her own ears it sounded remarkably like an accusation.

He grinned, white, healthy teeth gleaming. 'I got my secretary, Miss Ashton, to do it. Luckily, or unluckily, depending on how you view things, she has to take some time off to care for her elderly mother, so I need a replacement secretary.'

But he was looking at her the way a man looked at a woman he wanted, not the way a boss looked at his secretary.

If he'd been anyone in the firm, from a junior manager to one of the higher executives, *anyone* other than who he was, Laura would have been delighted. Now she was both confused and wary.

'Why did you ask for me?'

'Well, it was either that or take up plumbing.'

She refused to answer his teasing smile.

Ruefully, he queried, 'You're not altogether happy about it?'

'I'm very happy to *work* for you, Mr Carlson,' she replied stiffly.

'But not to sleep with me?'

Thrown by his honesty, his refusal to wrap things up, and by the strength of the magnetism that drew her to him, she stammered, 'Y-you're going much too fast for me.'

'Very well, then,' he said reasonably, 'we'll take things a bit slower. Begin by having dinner with me tonight.'

Wanting to accept, but knowing she ought to be cautious, she shook her head.

'Why not?'

Having no answer prepared, she spoke the exact truth. 'Because I'm a nobody from the general office, and you're Tane Carlson.'

'Would you accept my invitation if I were just another employee?'

'Yes.'

His eyes glinted dangerously. 'So I'm to be penalised because of who I am?' Getting no answer, he changed tack. 'Did you like the flowers?'

Laura drew a deep breath. No wonder when she'd tried to thank him David had denied sending two lots, declaring there must have been some mix-up on the florist's part.

'Yes, thank you, they were lovely,' she said remotely.

'What's the matter?' he asked suddenly. 'You're not married or engaged or anything? You're not wearing any rings. Is there someone special? Someone I'm going to have to wrest you from?'

The last sentence had been added in a joking fashion, but she felt oddly convinced that he was in earnest, that he would set about wresting her from the devil himself should it prove necessary.

'*Is* there someone special?' he persisted.

'No,' she answered breathlessly, 'there's no one.'

He smiled at her, such a blaze of light in his blue-grey eyes that her heart seemed to turn right over and she found herself smiling back. She heard his quick intake of breath before he said, 'That's the first time I've seen you smile.' Then, as if the knowledge delighted him, 'I didn't know you had twin dimples.' Suddenly, urgently, he added, 'Forget who I am—take a chance and have dinner with me.'

Succumbing to the fascination that gripped her, Laura agreed, 'All right.' But as soon as the words were spoken a doubt surfaced and pricked, uncomfortable as a burr.

Reading her expression, Tane queried, 'Now what's wrong?'

She looked at him with a steady gaze and asked bluntly, 'Are you married?'

'Is that a proposal?'

'An attempt at self-preservation. I don't want to get caught in the old trap.'

A slight frown pulling his dark, level brows together, he echoed, 'Old trap? Which old trap?'

'The boss tells secretary, "My wife doesn't understand" trap.'

'My wife doesn't...' he began slowly and, when Laura's eyes widened, he grinned '...exist. I am not married. I've never been married, and up until a week ago I had no intention of ever getting married.' Lightly he added, 'Now I may need to reconsider the matter.'

Stretching out his hand, he picked up a tendril of her hair which had escaped, and rubbed the glossy strands between his finger and thumb. 'Your hair is like spun silk; it looks as if it's trapped and held by the summer sunlight.'

Awkwardly, she said, 'It's very fine, and a problem to keep neat. Sometimes it drives me mad.'

'It could well have the same effect on me. I'd like to take out the pins and let it tumble around your shoulders, run my fingers through it while I kiss you... In fact I feel a divine madness coming on right at this moment...'

'Fight it,' she advised with a flippancy she was far from feeling, and sighed with relief when one of the phones in the boardroom began to ring.

As Tane grimaced and went to answer it, the door opened and a middle-aged woman with short iron-grey hair and a plain, no-nonsense face walked in.

'Miss Peters?' she said. 'I'm Lola Ashton. Sorry to be late, but I had to wait until the daily help came before I could leave my mother. Has Mr Carlson explained the situation?'

Laura answered, 'Briefly.'

'I'll be coming in for an hour or two each day until you get the hang of things.' Giving Laura a shrewd but not unfriendly look, she added, 'I did suggest to Mr Carlson that he borrow a more experienced secretary, but he said he was sure you could cope.'

'I'll do my best,' Laura promised.

The work had been nowhere near as difficult as she'd feared and, seeing she *could* cope, Lola Ashton had soon left her to it.

Laura's main problem had been making herself concentrate. With Tane Carlson sitting opposite, it had proved to be no easy task. Though during office hours he'd been disciplined and businesslike, which had helped to some extent...

A loud and determined rattling of the shop door-handle brought Laura to her feet. Dazedly she looked at her watch. Finding it was almost twenty to three, she hurried to push up the catch and open the door.

The middle-aged woman who was hovering on the threshold said huffily, 'I thought Friday shouldn't be half-closing day.'

'No, it isn't. I'm so sorry,' Laura apologised. Adding, 'In fact I don't normally *have* a half-closing day.'

Sniffing, still offended at being kept waiting, the woman headed for the 'Hobbies and Handicrafts' section.

Just after six o'clock, with only one customer sorting leisurely through the romances, Laura made herself a cup of tea and, picking up the phone, dialled Molly's number. She made a habit of calling each evening to be sure all was well with Jamie.

Because of the 'Lending Library' section, which provided a good part of her income, she needed to keep the shop open until seven-thirty each night. That made it very difficult to see her young son, except on Sundays.

At first, missing him dreadfully, she'd made the journey to Molly's several evenings a week. But soon common sense had told her it wasn't fair to the child to disturb his routine by keeping him up past his bedtime. And a lesser but still important consideration had been how much money was being drained from their already slender resources by bus fares.

When Molly had reported cheerfully that everything was fine, she asked, 'Are *you* all right?' Adding shrewdly, 'You sound a bit rattled.'

Just for a moment Laura was tempted to unburden herself, then, knowing she couldn't bear to talk about Tane, she answered steadily, 'I'm tired, that's all.'

Molly grunted, clearly unconvinced. 'Here's Jamie to say goodnight to you.'

Laura said her usual, 'Goodnight and God bless, darling. Be a good boy, won't you?'

As usual, his participation consisted only of listening and heavy breathing, but at least it gave her a feeling of closeness.

'It never fails to amaze me,' Molly said, again as usual, 'how a child who never stops talking won't utter a word when you want him to!'

By the time seven-thirty came Laura was sinking. She'd had nothing to eat since her breakfast toast, and she felt empty and a trifle sick. When the last customer had finished choosing a stack of library books, she followed him to the door, intent on locking up.

As she was about to drop the catch, a tall, dark man appeared from nowhere and pushed his way in. Heart lurching, Laura protested, 'I'm just closing.'

'Not before time,' Tane said grimly.

Though she hadn't admitted it openly, subconsciously she had *known* Tane hadn't finished with her, had *known* he would be back. So much hate had to find an outlet. She shivered.

'Do you always work so late?' he asked.

'Yes.' She refused to elaborate.

'What's that husband of yours thinking of to let you?'

She didn't answer.

Earlier he'd been wearing a smart business suit; now he was casually dressed in donkey-brown cords and a lightweight jacket. Hands thrust into his pockets, he strolled through the shop, looking about him with the throw-away arrogance of someone who owned the place.

When he reached the low door at the end, Laura said sharply, 'That's private.'

Taking his hands from his pockets, he raised a dark brow. 'Really?'

'Yes, really,' she returned tightly.

With one hand he opened the door, and with the other propelled her into the little back room, following closely on her heels.

While she tugged at the gold chain and fumed help-lessly, he looked around with an expression of disapprobation.

It was shabby and cramped, and, though Laura had painted the walls apricot-white, with only one small, heavily glazed window, the room was perpetually gloomy.

A wooden table and chair, a couch and a sagging arm-chair were arranged on the threadbare carpet. An old gas fire stood on the chipped and broken tiles of the hearth. On one side of it was a chest of drawers piled high with books, while on the other a long cupboard served as a wardrobe and store place. A stone sink with a water-heater, a battered wall-fridge and a couple of gas rings did duty as the kitchen.

There were two doors on the left. Tane opened both, peering first into a tiny enclosed yard, then into an anti-quated bathroom.

Laura closed her eyes, visualising with shame the badly worn lino, the claw-footed bath, rust-stained and water-marked, the cracked washbasin...

Withdrawing his head, he remarked disgustedly, 'What a dump!'

'No one asked you to come here,' she flashed.

He moved towards her and she stepped back hastily, her face losing colour.

'Are you afraid of me?' he demanded.

More than anything she needed to keep command of herself. Lifting her head, she looked at him steadily. 'Do I need to be?'

'Yes, I rather think you do.'

His reply shook her, as it had been meant to.

After a thoughtful inspection of the narrow divan which was made up as a bed, Tane asked interestedly, 'Tell me, where does your husband sleep?'

Her voice ragged, she informed him, 'That's none of your business... I wish you'd go. You've no right to be here.'

Cool as the proverbial cucumber, he smiled. 'Now there's where we disagree.'

While she stared at him, he went on, 'I've been talking to Perry...'

William Perry, her landlord, was bull-necked and overweight, with thick lips and bold blue eyes. He fancied himself as a ladies' man and, after several unpleasant encounters, when on each occasion he'd tried to make a pass at her, Laura had done her utmost to stay out of his way.

'It's funny,' Tane went on deliberately, 'but *he* didn't know you had a husband. He thinks you live here alone.'

'So long as I pay my rent it's none of his business either,' she said spiritedly. Then, with a sudden unease, 'Why were you talking to Perry?'

Ignoring Laura's question, Tane lifted her coat from a hook behind the door and held it ready. 'Slip this on; we're going out for a meal.'

'I don't want to go out for a meal.'

'Ah, but it isn't what *you* want. It's what *I* want.' With calm certainty he added, 'You see, I hold the whip hand.'

CHAPTER TWO

'IF YOU think I'm going to crawl to you...'

'You may need to.' Tane's voice held a quiet threat.

Laura hesitated, then, defeated by something within herself that couldn't oppose his compelling personality, allowed him to help her on with the coat. Obeying his mocking gesture, she preceded him through the shop and out on to the pavement, where a freshening breeze was chivvying pieces of litter along the gutter and pouncing gleefully on the wildly flapping pages of a discarded newspaper.

Tane's white Mercedes was a short distance down the street at a parking meter. He unlocked the door and, a hand beneath her elbow, settled her into the front passenger-seat.

'When did you last eat?' he asked, as he slid in beside her.

'Breakfast time,' she admitted.

'If you neglect yourself like this, no wonder your eyes look too big for your face.' He sounded curt, almost angry.

Laura said nothing. Just at that moment she felt too tired to argue, to make the point that she would have eaten her lunch if it hadn't been for *him*.

On the outskirts of town he stopped at a small basement restaurant. Though it was quiet and modest-looking, it appeared to be full, but as soon as he gave his name they were shown to an empty alcove table at the far end of the room.

'Do you fancy anything in particular?' he asked, after they had been served with a light dry sherry.

When Laura shook her head, without consulting the menu, he ordered tournedos Rossini for them both.

The service was quick and unobtrusive, and the dish appeared before them as if by magic. Laura still felt a little nauseous, but after the first few mouthfuls her stomach settled and she found she was ravenous. It was a long time since she'd tasted food like it, and she ate with delicate zest.

Glancing up, she found Tane's eyes were fixed on her. His plate was scarcely touched and she guessed he had been watching her all the while. Feeling like a greedy child, she flushed hotly. Instantly he looked down, making her realise he was sorry to have disturbed her, and they continued to eat in silence.

Despite the powerful chemistry—the fierce attraction between Tane and herself which had always made Laura feel breathless and excited—in the past they had been easy together, talking constantly, *communicating*.

Even on the very first evening he had taken her out, the ice had been quickly broken...

Sitting in a quiet corner of his favourite restaurant, he had smiled lazily at her and invited, 'Tell me about yourself.'

Suddenly uncomfortable, she had looked down at the hands clasped together in her lap.

He was the head of a business empire which had world-wide assets, an influential man with a wealthy background. She was a nobody—a junior secretary with a monthly wage packet and a flat in a distinctly seedy area.

When he had called for her that evening, she'd realised with a jolt how very out of place his sleek car looked parked in Royal Street.

'Shame!' he said suddenly, clicking his tongue.

Laura looked at him blankly.

'How long have you had a speech problem?' he queried in a kindly tone.

She wrinkled her nose at him, then asked reluctantly, 'What do you want to know?'

'Everything. Start with your family.'

'I . . . I haven't any family. When I was seven years old my parents let me go to the seaside for a week with a friend, while they had a holiday in Spain. They never came back. The plane crashed on take-off.'

'So who brought you up?'

'I had no close relatives, no one who wanted me, so I was put in a children's home.'

He waited for her to go on, those bewitching smoky eyes on her face.

'I hated it.' The words came out in a rush. 'Perhaps if I'd been younger I'd have settled better. But I was terribly unhappy. I used to wish I'd been on the plane with Mum and Dad.'

Reaching across the table, Tane took her hand, as if comforting the child she'd once been.

'No one at the home was unkind to me,' she hastened to explain. 'Just the opposite in fact. They made arrangements for me to go out once a month and spend a weekend with a very nice couple.

'Mr and Mrs Cartwright had five children of their own and a lovely big house and garden. Theirs was such a close, happy family . . .

'Somehow that only made things worse. You see, I never felt as if I *belonged*. I was always on the outside looking in, a spectator.

'After a few visits I asked not to go again. But I couldn't really explain *why*. Mrs Cartwright was terribly upset. She thought I was very ungrateful...'

Tane squeezed the slim fingers he was still holding. Laura managed a shaky smile. 'I don't know why it still bothers me. It's all in the past, over and done with.'

'The past is never over and done with,' he corrected. 'It's the past that scars us, makes us what we are today.'

There was a sudden harshness in Tane's voice, a bleakness in his face, that convinced her *his* childhood couldn't have been a very happy one.

As though reading her thoughts, he explained briefly, 'My parents were divorced.'

'Have you any brothers or sisters?' she ventured.

'No. I was an only child, and even, at that, one too many.'

Before she could ask him what he meant, the bitterness was gone, wiped away as if it had never been, and he went on smoothly, 'But we were talking about *you*. Did you make any lasting friends inside the orphanage?'

'Yes, one. David Belmont. Although he was a year older than me, he was small for his age, and timid. Most of the other boys either ignored him or picked on him.

'To survive in that kind of environment, a child needs to be tough. Neither of us was.'

'Yet you did survive.'

'Of course.' She smiled.

He released her hand and refilled her wine glass. 'What happened after you left the orphanage?'

'I was found a room with an old dragon who frightened me half to death, and a job in a bookshop, which I loved. The wages were very low, but the owner of the shop, a small gnome-like man named Joseph Merryweather, taught me a lot about old books.

'Though I thoroughly enjoyed working in the shop, I wanted to earn more so I could make my escape from Mrs Gifford...'

He lifted one dark brow. 'The old dragon?'

She dimpled. 'Yes.'

'So what did you do?'

'I went to night-school to learn shorthand and typing and general business studies. It was fortunate I did, because Mr Merryweather died suddenly and the shop had to be closed.

'Quite by chance I saw that Roberts Engineering needed office staff, and I managed to get a job with them. When I'd been there a few months they sent me on a computing course, and I found myself sitting next to David.'

'The boy from the orphanage?'

Laura nodded. 'It must have been my lucky day. He knew of a small furnished flat that had just become vacant. A week later he helped me to move in. For the first time in my life I felt free, independent.'

It had been a wonderful feeling, and she'd determined never to give it up.

'Have you and David kept in touch?'

'Oh, yes. I sometimes wonder what I'd do without him.'

'What's he like? Describe him.'

'He's just a bit taller than I am, with fair hair, bright hazel eyes and a thin, intelligent face. He's kind and generous, a really *nice* person.'

'You sound as if you're fond of him?'

'I am,' she said quietly. 'Very fond.'

'This morning, in the office, you told me there was no one special.' The remark was made casually, but there seemed to be a definite tension in Tane's attitude.

'There isn't. At least not in the way you mean.'

'He's never asked you to marry him?'

Feeling rather like Jane Eyre being interrogated by Mr Rochester, Laura said, 'As a matter of fact he has, several times.'

'But you haven't accepted. Why?'

'Because I don't love him in that way. There's no passion there.'

'Ah...' Tane said softly. He lifted her hand and touched his lips to the inside of her wrist, sending little shivers through her, before asking, 'So when did you leave Roberts?'

Her voice not quite steady, Laura answered, 'About six months ago, when they were taken over by Telford's, most of the office staff became redundant and——'

'And fate brought you to me.'

Coming from anyone else that hackneyed phrase would have made her smile, but Tane had spoken the words so quietly, so gravely, almost as if they were a thanksgiving...

Laura blinked, dragged back to the present by the waiter bringing a cheese-board and coffee.

Having been helped to some superb Stilton, and a cup of excellent black coffee, she sighed, replete. His penetrating gaze on her face, Tane abruptly remarked, 'You look tired. Perhaps we should get on our way.'

Relieved, Laura watched him pay the bill. His mood appeared to have softened, and she began to hope that he meant just to drop her off at the shop and suspend hostilities, at least for tonight.

Once in his car she tossed her coat on to the rear seat, and, leaning back against the luxurious grey suede upholstery, closed her eyes.

The last few months had been a strain. She'd lived not only with the continual threat of sexual harassment, but also with a growing fear that she would be unable to meet her financial commitments.

Tane's sudden re-emergence into her life had been the last straw, threatening to make the weight of worry too heavy for her to bear. Her first impulse on seeing him again had been to run and keep running. Having Jamie, however, made that impossible. If she had been employed in an ordinary job she might have managed a disappearing trick. As things were, she was trapped, her small amount of capital, and borrowed money also, tied up in stock. So she *had* to stick it out.

Possibly all she needed was a chance to get her second wind. She was strong—hadn't she proved it in the past?—not one to give in. No, *somehow* she would manage, if only Tane would leave her alone...

When the car swished to a halt, Laura stirred and opened heavy lids. For a moment or two, still not fully awake, her brain struggled to believe the information being fed to it by her senses.

This was no city street. It was dark and quiet with the stillness of the country. Somewhere, a long way away, a dog barked, and, closer, an owl called, tu-whit, tu-whoo-hoo-hoo, with melancholy mirth.

Struggling up, she demanded, 'Where are we? This isn't town.'

He got out and came round to open her door.

'Where are we?' she repeated, without moving.

'Marsh House,' he replied. 'It's a few miles south of the hamlet of Thorncliffe.'

He'd answered her question, yet not answered it.

'But where...?'

'I suggest you get out,' he said levelly, 'and we'll talk inside.'

Her thoughts darting about like frightened minnows, she sat tight.

'I don't want to have to use force...' He didn't finish the sentence, but his tone implied that he was quite prepared to employ coercion if necessary.

After hesitating for a few seconds, seeing nothing else for it, Laura climbed stiffly out, to find they were parked in front of a low, rambling building. A hotchpotch of gables and crooked chimneys loomed black against the sky, which hung like a huge inverted bowl of indigo pricked with stars.

The countryside was flat, the fields dotted with the pale shapes of sheep, while some distance away a group of twisted thorn trees stood out in dark silhouette. Not another dwelling was in sight. Very faintly, carried on the night air, a church clock chimed the witching hour.

With an arm around her waist, Tane urged her towards the house, pausing only to steady her as, still dazed and not in full command of her faculties, she stumbled.

When he'd unlocked the heavy, studded door he pushed her inside, switching on the light to show a large, flagged hall with doors going off in all directions and a central oak staircase leading up to a carved wooden gallery. A door to the left opened into a comfortable, chintzy sitting-room.

He steered her towards a chair, but, refusing to sit down, she turned to face him, as if at bay. Suddenly she was suffocatingly aware of his *maleness*, his imposing height and the width of his shoulders; her legs began to tremble, her skin felt flushed and clammy and her pulse-rate quickened alarmingly.

'I don't know what you've brought me here for——' she began.

'Don't you?' he broke in softly, suggestively. When her blue eyes dilated, he smiled, a cruel little twist to his sculptured lips.

Not really believing he meant to rape her, but afraid all the same, Laura gulped in air. 'If you think——'

'I think it's time we went to bed. It's after midnight.'

Her hand to her throat, fingers tugging at the thin chain, she begged, 'Oh, please, Tane...'

Ignoring her plea, he went on, 'But we'll just clear up one thing first.' He lifted her left hand and twisted the plain gold ring on her third finger round and round. 'Why are you pretending to be married?'

Her heart was beating with great heavy thuds and it was difficult to breathe. Somehow she gasped, 'I'm not pretending. I am married.'

Gripping her shoulders, his fingers biting in, he shook her furiously. 'Damn you, don't lie to me!'

Her head snapped back and then lolled like a rag-doll's. Then, as suddenly as he'd seized her, he let her go, thrusting his hands deep into his pockets as if unable to trust himself to keep them off her.

Her face white as cherry blossom, every ounce of strength drained from her limbs, Laura swayed and would have fallen if he hadn't caught and supported her.

She was vaguely aware that he muttered something unintelligible, then she was lifted effortlessly and carried up the stairs.

He laid her on a bed and, having removed her sandals, began to undo the buttons that ran down the front of her shirtwaister.

Head swimming, she lay still and limp, her eyes closed, instinctively sure that helplessness was her only means of defence. To struggle would be useless, and her resistance would only inflame his anger and passion.

The buttons and belt dealt with, her shoulders were raised and her arms freed, the dress was eased from beneath her, and then, as she held her breath, a light covering of clothes was pulled up to her chin. She heard soft footsteps retreating, followed by the click of a light-switch and the sound of a door being quietly closed.

Relief, potent as a drug, washed warmly, soothingly over her. She couldn't have borne it if he had taken in hate and anger what she'd always given with such love and joy...

From the moment they met their coming together had been inevitable. Like a lightning strike, the flame Tane had kindled had taken hold, and with frightening speed turned into a blaze, a forest fire over which she had no control.

If he hadn't been an experienced and sophisticated man more than ten years older than herself, she might have believed they were both caught up in the conflagration. As it was, she'd hardly dared credit that he was as consumed, as overwhelmed, as she was.

They had gone to shows and concerts, to museums and art galleries, and, sharing a passion for literature, browsed around old bookshops for hours on end.

As winter had given way to a warm, blossom-bowed spring they'd spent weekends in the country, sometimes walking for miles and eating at village pubs, other times picnicking and lazing by cool riverbanks.

Although she worked for him by day and saw him almost every night and most weekends, she'd never grown tired of his company.

Aware that, though discreet in his dealings with women, he had had a succession of mistresses, she'd half expected that he would soon press her to sleep with him. But, though he'd watched her continuously and frequently touched her, he'd seldom kissed her, and when he had it was with a restraint that made it clear he was keeping his feelings on a tight leash.

Scarcely knowing what to think, she'd begun to hope that what he felt for her was more than just a physical thing...that he might even love her.

Then, one evening in May, after they'd dined out, he'd taken her back to his penthouse for the first time. She hadn't been surprised to find it was in Hunwick Court, a luxury block close to Hyde Park.

While he'd fixed them both a drink she'd looked around the comfortable but wholly masculine room, liking the simplicity of the oatmeal walls and carpet, and the dark brown suite.

They had sat side by side on the low couch, sipping brandy without speaking. His face in profile had a sort of stark male beauty that did strange things to her pulse-rate.

Usually any break in their conversation was contented, companionable, but tonight the silence was heavy with an unmistakable sexual tension. She tried to lighten it by querying, 'How did you come to be called Tane? It's an unusual name.'

He'd never spoken about his childhood, and when the conversation seemed to be drifting that way he'd always deftly steered it into other channels.

Now he said, 'I was born in New Zealand. Tane is a Maori name. Most people in England say it to rhyme with mane, but the Maoris pronounce every letter, which makes it Tarné.' His reply was abstracted, his mind clearly on neither the question nor the answer.

There was another weighted silence. Then all at once he took the goblet from her hand, set it down with great deliberation on the small table by his elbow, and turned to look at her.

She gazed into that strong face, loving its hard planes and angles, its beautifully sculptured mouth, its straight nose and squared-off chin. When finally she looked into those blue-grey eyes, the expression in their smoky depths turned her very bones to water. As he drew her into his arms her lips parted on a sigh.

Easing her back against the soft cushions, he kissed her with a hunger that seemed to draw her very soul from her body. In that instant any defences she might have subconsciously tried to keep intact crumbled.

She was his and he knew it.

He kissed her face, her closed eyelids, her temples, her throat, while his fingers unfastened the neat covered buttons on her blouse. As he buried his face against the warm swell of her breasts she made a small sound, a cross between a gasp and a groan. Every inch of her skin was acutely sensitive—his warm breath made her shiver, and her nipples firmed and ached for his touch.

He released the front fastening of her dainty bra and, eyes closed, dark lashes lying on his cheeks, let his mouth travel over the soft curves, blindly seeking, until it found its goal and he suckled sweetly as a child, while she gasped and shuddered at the exquisite feelings he was causing.

When his fingers moved to fondle the other waiting breast, the sensations he was wringing from her were so close to torture that Laura whispered raggedly, 'I can't stand it.'

He laughed softly. 'My heart's darling, this is only the overture.'

The overture to ecstasy, to becoming his lover, the latest of his string of mistresses.

His willingness to bide his time, his patience, had given rise to the hope that *she* might be different, *special*. Now she knew she was just like all the rest.

Pain lanced through her at the thought, pain that showed clearly in her face.

Frowning, he asked gently, 'What's the matter? Don't you want to make love with me?'

Her usual honesty brought the truth. 'You must know I do. But I . . . I'm not cut out for affairs.'

'How do you know? Have you had any?'

She shook her head.

He lifted her chin and looked deep into her eyes. 'None?'

'None.' She laughed shakily. 'I suppose that sounds very dull and prudish, but I . . . well, I've never been tempted before. I'm sorry if you——'

His kiss stopped her words, then, with careful fingers, he fastened her bra clip and re-buttoned her blouse, tidying her the way a parent tidied a child, before saying, 'I'd better take you home.'

His manner was now so cool that she wondered if he had finished with her. Perhaps he only liked experienced women? Perilously close to tears, she found herself unable to ask him, unable to speak at all.

Catching her underlip in her teeth, she wished fervently that she'd kept silent. If she had, she would still be in his arms, transported into a magical world of passion and delight.

For as long as it lasted.

After a journey during which neither spoke, he left her at her door without even a kiss.

'Tane...' He was turning away when she breathed his name. 'Will I see you tomorrow?'

He regarded her quizzically. 'Were you thinking of taking the day off work?'

The following morning he appeared to be his normal self and, when he suggested that, as it was Friday, they might slip away from the office early and spend their weekend in the country, the terrible constriction around her heart loosened. For the rest of the day she sang under her breath as she went through the now routine tasks.

They left mid-afternoon, stopping off at Royal Mansions so that Laura could push a few necessities into an overnight bag, and then they were speeding out of town in a bid to beat the home-going rush.

'I've booked us in at the Little Mermaid in Church Paton,' Tane told her.

Uncaring where they went, her heart carolling joyously because they were together and going *somewhere*, she said gaily, 'Sounds lovely.'

Though the countryside they were driving through was lovely, more often than not Laura's gaze was fixed on the man by her side.

Tane's features were handsome and clean-cut, the bone-structure strong and well defined. His peat-dark hair was thick and springy, the ends curling behind the neat scroll-work of his ears and into his neck. He looked fit and healthy and virile.

Aware of her scrutiny, he turned to smile at her.

His eyes and mouth were *fascinating*, she thought; they would have made the most commonplace man exciting. And he was far from commonplace.

When they reached the Little Mermaid, a black and white half-timbered inn on the outskirts of a small, picturesque village, Laura found that Tane had booked separate rooms, as he usually did.

It seemed they were back on their old footing.

After a walk and a late meal they climbed the wooden stairs and he followed her into her room, which lay under the eaves. It was quaint and old-fashioned, with a faded patchwork quilt on the big bed, and sheets that smelled faintly of lavender. The casement windows, with their diamond-leaded panes, were thrown open to the balmy night air.

After staring out towards a distant copse, etched dark against the sky, Tane turned abruptly to look at her. Something in his face made her breath catch in her throat, but his voice was level, almost casual, as he asked, 'Will you marry me?'

She stood and gaped at him stupidly.

'Laura...?' Her name was an appeal, and his expression showed he was waiting for her answer with almost painful intensity.

She was so choked with gladness all she could do was nod.

He gathered her into his arms and just held her tightly, his cheek against her hair. When at last he kissed her, freed from the fear that she was to be only another affair, she returned his kiss with ardour, with a feeling of utter *rightness*, melting against him, holding nothing back.

If he had intended to wait until they were married to take her to bed, her innocent fervour was his undoing.

'You don't mind that I...that I've never...? I mean, it sounds so *old-fashioned*.'

Realising what she was trying to say, he told her joyfully, 'It sounds *wonderful*. In the past I've never cared one way or the other about the women I've known. But from the start I wanted *you* to be different, to be as sweetly innocent as you looked.

'I know it's the old double standard, and I've no right to expect something from you that I can't give... All the same——' He broke off, his voice not altogether steady, and kissed her deeply before lifting her on to the high bed.

Though she was inexperienced, Laura was an equal partner, meeting and matching his passion with her own. Theirs was a joyful union, a union of fire and light and exhilaration.

She gloried in his passionate wooing of her mind and body, his masterful skill and tenderness, in the knowledge that he found her as wholly enchanting as she found him. He was everything and more than she'd ever dreamt of in a lover.

It was towards dawn when, utterly content, they lay in each other's arms, and he said huskily, 'We'll get married as soon as possible. There's no reason to wait. You haven't any close relatives and, apart from an aunt who lives in Northumberland, neither have I, so we can make it a very quiet wedding... But I'm being a selfish swine. Perhaps you want a white dress and all the trimmings?'

Pressing her face against the smooth, tanned column of his throat, giving him butterfly kisses with her eyelashes, Laura murmured, 'I don't want any trimmings—only you.'

He chuckled. 'I'm glad you said that. However, I think we should have a nice long honeymoon. Don't you agree?'

She gave a contented little grunt.

His lips muffled in her hair, he asked, 'Have you ever been abroad?'

'While I worked at Roberts Engineering I went with a group of the girls on a ten-day package tour to Crete. It was marvellous...hot and sunny.' Dreamily she added, 'I've always loved islands.'

'How do you fancy a hot, sunny month in the Seychelles?'

Happy beyond her wildest dreams, she agreed, 'It sounds like heaven.' But a cold, wet month in West Hartlepool would be heaven so long as Tane was with her...

A sound somewhere near at hand startled her, setting her thoughts to flight. She sat bolt upright, staring into the darkness, her heart hammering against her ribs. It was a moment or two before she realised the noise had come from the room next door. Sinking back on to the pillows, she closed her eyes and, worn out physically and emotionally, was asleep within seconds.

Laura awoke slowly, reluctantly, as if from a shipwreck, feeling threatened and apprehensive, her mind and spirit thrown into nervous disorder. Unwilling to move, to face what lay ahead, she stayed for a while staring at the white ceiling before sitting up.

It was nearly nine o'clock, and a lovely summer day. Sun poured through the mullioned windows and spread in a golden swath across the old, flower-strewn carpet.

On either side of the wood-panelled walls was a door. Getting out of bed, she cautiously opened the nearest, and found, to her surprise, a modern, well-appointed bathroom.

Her eyes widened to see an elegant oatmeal-coloured blouse and skirt had been placed on a stool, along with a neat pile of beautiful lace-edged undies. She picked up a delicate peach bra and found it was exactly her size, and obviously brand new.

He must have bought the clothes before coming to the shop, so it had been no spur-of-the-moment decision to bring her here, but a carefully planned *abduction*.

Every nerve in Laura's body tightened, and it took a great effort of will to regain some composure. While she showered she tried to think objectively, to decide what Tane's intentions were, what he really wanted. But nothing made any sense, nothing was clear except the fact that he hated her.

That was what shocked and terrified her, that and the violence she'd unwittingly aroused. Had he really intended to rape her? she wondered. Or had he been merely frightening her?

Now she was less tired, more in control, she felt convinced it was the latter.

Having dried herself, she hesitated over the undies, unwilling to replace the ones she'd slept in, equally reluctant to wear the set he'd bought. Finally, half despising herself, she put on the new ones.

It was a long time since she'd been able to afford anything but the cheapest cotton or nylon, and the brush of real silk against her skin had a luxurious feel that made her very conscious of her own body.

Ignoring the blouse and skirt, she donned her cotton shirtwaister and sandals, and combed the smooth fall of hair which curled on to her shoulders. Normally it was an unremarkable ash-brown but, as Tane had once observed—though in a more poetic way—it wasn't colour-fast, and the sun had put blonde streaks in it, and added gold tips to her long lashes.

The mirrored face gazing back at her looked pale and strained, and there were shadows like bruises beneath the almond eyes. After replacing the comb, she still lingered, staring at the daisy-patterned tiles, until, ashamed of her cowardice, she squared her shoulders and made her way along the polished gallery and down the stairs.

CHAPTER THREE

THE appetising smell of percolating coffee drew Laura to the kitchen. She peered in to find the table set with a yellow checked cloth, and Tane, a matching tea-towel knotted around his lean hips, basting a pan of eggs, while bacon sizzled beneath the grill.

Without looking up, he said, 'Good timing. I was just about to call you.' Blandly, he added, 'I hope you slept well?'

Equally blandly, she replied, 'Very well, thank you.'

He pulled out a chair and poured her an orange juice, which she sipped as he dished up breakfast.

'I didn't know you were so domesticated,' she remarked, faintly mocking.

Discarding the tea-towel, he told her, 'There's quite a lot you don't know about me. A side you haven't yet seen.'

The softly spoken words had a menacing ring which sent icy little shivers chasing down her spine. He was wearing beige trousers and a black turtle-neck sweater, and he looked big and tough and formidable. Scared, but determined not to show it, she put on a look of cool indifference, and picked up her knife and fork.

During the meal Tane kept the conversation light and impersonal, as if this were just a commonplace situation and nothing untoward had occurred.

Not yet ready to go into battle, she followed his lead. While she ate she watched him surreptitiously, and it was as though a flame sprang up inside her. If she saw

43

him every day for the rest of her life, his hard face, with its striking planes and angles, its chiselled lips and handsome, thickly lashed eyes, would still move and excite her.

If she saw him every day for the rest of her life...

The last time they'd breakfasted together she'd looked forward to just that, glowing with happiness, knowing a lifetime spent in each other's company wouldn't be too long, and sure that he felt the same...

As if he couldn't wait to see her wearing his ring, the minute they'd returned to town he'd taken her to Morton King and bought her a diamond solitaire—a magnificent starburst that flashed with brilliant white fire. Though not a man to make any display of affection in public, after slipping it on to her finger, Tane had lifted her hand to his lips in a gesture of homage that had made her blue eyes sparkle with tears.

Their wedding day set for just over a month's time, she'd needed no persuasion to give up her poky flat and move into Tane's penthouse.

David had proved to be the only stumbling-block.

As soon as he'd returned from his computing course, she had told him about Tane. Seeing his fair face darken, she'd emphasised that the relationship was an innocent one.

Believing her, he'd looked dubious, as if wondering what a man like Tane Carlson would want with an *innocent* relationship. When she'd broken the news that they were getting married, David had taken it with good grace, saying he was very happy for her. But when he'd discovered she was giving up her flat, he'd begged, 'Don't do it. Don't move in with him before the wedding.'

'What do you expect him to do,' she'd asked teasingly, 'change his mind and leave me at the altar?'

Seriously, David had answered, 'I don't think you should commit yourself until the ring's on your finger.'

'It's too late,' she'd admitted.

'You mean he's already seduced you?' There was bitterness in David's tone.

'I mean we're already lovers,' she corrected gently.

He looked pale and ill, and she hated the thought of upsetting him. To try and put his mind at rest she suggested that the two men should get to know each other. But, with a vehemence that was quite out of character, David refused even to meet Tane.

With their wedding only a couple of weeks away, Laura and Tane spent another long, idyllic weekend at the Little Mermaid.

On Sunday afternoon, before starting back to town, they took a walk through the woods above the village. Hand in hand, discussing their wedding plans, they were descending a winding, steepish lane with a straggle of cottages on either side, when a boy of perhaps five or six shot past them on a bright red cycle that was clearly too big for him. He had disappeared round the next bend when a sharp squeal of brakes was followed by a rending crash and the scraping of metal on stone.

They hurried round the corner to see the bicycle lying on its side, one wheel still spinning, and scrape marks on the lane's metalled surface. The boy, who was just picking himself up, had begun to cry lustily.

Laura crouched by his side to see how much damage had been done, and discovered that the fleshy part of both palms was skinned and blood was running from a deep graze on his left knee. She felt in her bag for a handful of tissues and, with a comforting arm around him, began to staunch the flow of blood, all the time talking soothingly. When his sobs had abated somewhat, she wiped his nose and asked, 'Where do you live?'

He didn't answer, and she was about to repeat the question when a shrill voice called, 'Danny...? Danny...?' and a harassed-looking woman appeared. 'I told you not to go out of the garden,' she scolded. 'I don't know what your dad'll say. You might have finished up under a car. Oh, *look* at you!'

'I don't think he's badly hurt,' Laura hastened to assure her.

'And just look at your new bike!' Picking up the cycle, she started to wheel it up the hill. Danny let out a wail and began to limp pathetically after her. The woman hesitated.

Laura glanced at Tane, who was standing in the background looking withdrawn and aloof, and, answering her unspoken appeal, he lifted the boy and carried him back up the hill.

It was a minute or so before he returned, and when he did he looked put out, rattled, as though annoyed by the intrusion into their bliss.

Making no comment about what had happened, he resumed their earlier conversation. Laura followed his lead, and by the time they'd reached the village he was himself again.

But the little incident left her with a strange feeling of unease which, though it diminished over the next few days, didn't quite die.

The following Friday evening they ate in the penthouse, Laura preparing a simple meal of omelettes and salad, followed by cheese and fruit.

Sitting on the couch, she sipped her coffee, and involuntarily her gaze strayed to where Tane stood looking out of the window towards Hyde Park. Tall and muscular, with a superb physique, if he hadn't had an excellent brain for business, he could have earned his living as a prize-fighter or a lumberjack. For despite his height he was a man who was never awkward, who moved lightly, easily, who was *aware*—a charismatic man who not only gave pleasure to the eye, but also whose character charmed and expanded the mind. A man among men.

And he loved her. She was his woman.

She had never been so happy in the whole of her life, Laura thought. Each day the mirror showed her she fairly glowed, and she could see a matching glow in Tane. It suited him. His eyes alight, his mouth warm, ready to smile, he looked more handsome, more vitally alive than ever.

While they felt as they did about each other they were invulnerable: no one and nothing could touch them or spoil their perfect happiness.

As if she'd sent him an unspoken message, he turned, and they smiled at each other. He came over to sit beside her, putting an arm around her shoulders. She shivered with the delicious excitement his nearness always caused, and snuggled closer.

For a while they just sat in harmony, then Laura asked the question that had been hovering at the back of her mind. 'Tane, where will we live when we're married?'

He raised a dark brow. 'Don't you like it here?'

With its spacious rooms, its sunny patio and leafy roof-garden the penthouse was a very pleasant place to live.

'Yes, yes, of course I do, but I . . .'

'You can redecorate and re-furnish if you want.' He grinned with a flash of white teeth. 'I'm sure you're not the type to cover everything in pink frills.'

'It's not that,' she said, staring down at her pale, shiny, oval nails. 'It's just . . . well, the penthouse is fine for the time being, but it would be nice to have a house in the country, with a real garden, for when we start a family.'

His absolute stillness made her lift her head and look at him. Somehow, without ever having discussed it, she'd taken it for granted that he felt as she did. Now, with dawning apprehension, she asked carefully, 'You do want children, don't you?'

'No, I don't want children.'

'You mean, not yet?'

He could have put her off with qualifications, with vague promises of 'sometime', but, honest as she was, he said uncompromisingly, 'I mean not at all. Never.'

'Perhaps you haven't given it enough thought,' she ventured.

Jumping up, he strode to the window. His broad back half turned, he said icily, 'I've given it plenty of thought. I don't want any children.'

'W-why not?' she stammered. Then, flushed and troubled, asked, 'I mean is there any reason . . .?'

He swung to face her. 'There aren't any problems regarding my health or ability to have children, if that's what you're asking. It's simply that I don't *like* children, and I don't *want* children.'

'But even if you don't care for children as such, surely you'd like your own?' she persisted.

Tightly, he answered, 'I've already said I wouldn't. Now can we close the subject?'

'No, Tane.' Somehow she managed to keep her voice steady. 'We have to talk about it.'

'I don't intend to have any children, so there's nothing further to be said.'

A grass roots *need* existed that was so deep, so much part of Laura's nature, that there seemed no room for compromise. Slowly she said, 'I can't marry you on those terms.'

His head came up.

Though shaken by the look on his face, she went on, 'I mean it. Maybe for a year or two I'd be happy. But I *know* that eventually I would long for a family. It's a fundamental part of marriage——'

'Nonsense!' he said curtly. 'Many women these days marry with no intention of having children, and they're quite happy.'

'Perhaps... I only know I'm not one of them. I wouldn't want to go into marriage without the hope of children.'

'Suppose you couldn't have any?'

'Then I'd try to adopt some.'

'You mean children are more important to you than a husband?'

She got to her feet and stood facing him. 'I don't mean anything of the sort. I only know I couldn't be truly happy without a family to love and care for.'

Savagely, he said, 'So you don't want *me*, you just want a father for your children?'

'Of course I want you!' she cried passionately. 'I want you as a friend and companion, as a lover and husband. I want to live my whole life with you, and die in your arms.'

'All of which sounds wonderful,' he said with searing bitterness. 'Except that you apparently want children more.'

'Not *more*, but——'

'Tell me something,' he interrupted tersely. 'If I *couldn't* have children, or there were some pressing reason *not* to have them, would you still marry me?'

She answered unhesitatingly, 'Yes.'

'But you're not prepared to marry me as things are?'

It was a bone-deep *basic* difference, a drastic divergence of beliefs and feelings and wants that couldn't be ignored or gilded over. Laura could marry him and hope to change his mind, or allow him to hope that he could change hers. But his aversion to children was clearly as strong and deep as her desire for them.

Such a fundamental difference was a rock on which sooner or later their marriage would founder, and she loved him far too much to cause him such unhappiness and grief. Far too much to risk spoiling his whole life.

'Well?' he demanded.

She looked him in the eyes and answered, 'No.'

Livid with anger, he snarled, 'Well, then, find yourself another stud.'

'Tane...!' She grasped his arm.

He shook her off, and before she could make any further attempt to detain him he was gone, the door slamming behind him with enough force to make the very air shiver.

For a long time she just stood there, then she dragged herself into their bedroom and, taking her cases from the shelf of the walk-in wardrobe, bundled her clothes in anyhow.

Dry-eyed, still too frozen for tears, she took the lift down and stumbled outside, the cases banging against her legs. It was raining hard, and the shoulders of the jacket she'd thrown on were soon wet through. If he was walking, Tane would get saturated, she thought desolately. He'd left without a coat of any kind.

All at once her face crumpled and she was sobbing aloud, open-mouthed, despairingly, like a child. She walked until, exhausted, she was forced to set the cases down just as a cruising taxi drew level. The grizzled driver jumped out and opened the door. Not knowing what else to do, she clambered in while he tossed her cases into the boot.

Back behind the wheel, he glanced over his shoulder to ask, 'Where to?' The tears still trickling, she just looked at him, not knowing where to go or what to do. Sympathetic to her distress without knowing the cause, he suggested, 'A hotel?'

'I...I don't...'

'What about a friend?'

'Yes...yes...' She choked out David's address and, sitting back, closed her eyes. When they got there, the kindly driver carried her cases right to the door and waited with her until it was opened.

David asked no questions. After taking one look at her stricken face, he put her to bed with a mug of hot milk and a couple of aspirin tablets.

Laura had very little recollection of the next few days. In a state of shock, she slept most of the time, and, even during the periods she was awake, the world was a twilight place. Like an automaton she ate and drank whatever she was given, but she no longer cared whether she lived or died.

It was David who finally jerked her out of that terrible lassitude. Putting down the bowl of soup he'd brought her with a little crash, he muttered, 'If that look of hopelessness doesn't go soon, I swear I'll kill the swine.'

Realising for the first time how much David was suffering because of her, she had begun to make the effort to take up her life again, trying desperately not to think of what *might* have been...

'Are you all right?' Tane's query held a swift urgency.

For a second or two Laura couldn't speak, then she answered steadily, 'Yes, I'm fine.' And indeed she felt nothing. It was as if, unable to cope with even the remembrance of such pain, her brain had decreed that all her emotions should be instantly freeze-dried.

His gaze remained on her lovely, poignant face, examining the prominent bones, the hollow cheeks, the fined-down look, before dropping to a more intimate study of the soft curves beneath her dress. 'You're too thin,' he observed at last.

'I was overweight when you knew me,' Laura demurred.

'You were perfect. Quite perfect.' There was a thickness in his voice that brought her head up.

'Oh, yes,' he said bitterly, 'I was crazy about you, besotted. You were my whole world.'

She flinched at the ice-cold fury in his eyes.

'How do you think I felt when I got home to find you'd disappeared?' When she stared at him mutely, he went on, 'I told myself you'd only gone out because you were angry and upset, that you'd be back, and then we could work *something* out...

'When I found you'd taken most of your clothes, but left your engagement ring and everything else I'd ever bought you, I should have known. But, though you'd made it clear how relatively unimportant I was to you, I was still idiotic enough to believe you wouldn't really leave me.

'Convinced you'd go into the office as usual, I waited for Monday morning like a cat on hot coals. When there was no sign of you I was shattered.

'I was only too well aware that you had no money and no place to live, and I did my utmost to find you. When all my enquiries drew a blank, I knew what it was like to be on the rack. I couldn't eat, I couldn't sleep...'

Unable to bear any more, Laura made a choked protest, an inarticulate plea for him to stop.

But relentlessly he went on, 'I had thought I knew what loneliness meant, what desolation felt like... You see, beneath the aura of success that everyone took to be happiness, I was a solitary man. I lived alone. If I took a mistress I kept her in a flat of her own. I never found any woman I could care for, or any I wanted to *live* with. Several swore they loved me, but what they meant was I was a satisfactory lover, and I gave them clothes and jewels and all the material things they wanted.

'Until I met you all I knew about love was how to live without it. You were sunshine in a cold, dark world, warmth that melted the grip of winter and made flowers bloom. You were everything I'd ever wanted or needed.

'The most wonderful thing, however—the *quintessence*—was that *you loved me*. Not my money, not my power, not my social position, not any of the things plenty of women would have married me for, but *me*.

'I preened myself. I thought, poor, stupid fool that I was, you would have married me if we'd only had bare boards to sleep on—that I meant more to you than anything or anybody on this earth.'

He had; oh, *he had*. If she hadn't loved him so much she would have married him in spite of the fact that they'd wanted different things from marriage, different lifestyles. Differences which she had believed, and *still* believed, were quite incompatible.

'Perhaps such blind bigotry needed stamping on...' he continued. 'But there's something particularly degrading, soul-destroying, about being seen solely as a stud, so my disillusionment and anger were on the same scale as my infatuation.'

He'd always seemed so strong, so self-sufficient, that she'd thought of him as a god, not as someone with a character as insecure and unpredictable as her own. Not as a lonely person, with faults and failings and needs...

'Crying, Laura? I'm afraid it's too late for remorse.'

Until he spoke she hadn't been aware that tears were running down her cheeks in a steady, silent stream. Now, in despair, she covered her face with her hands.

She had only thought of the break-up from her own point of view—what *she* had gone through. It had never occurred to her that Tane might have been just as wretched. Perhaps she hadn't truly believed in his love. She had supposed that when his anger had had time to abate he would take another mistress and put her out of his mind. She had never dreamt of him being badly hurt, *wounded*.

But she'd been wrong. He wouldn't be as embittered, wouldn't feel such black hatred, if he hadn't suffered.

She wiped her wet cheeks with her fingers, and, only too aware of how inadequate the words were, whispered, 'I'm sorry, so *sorry*. I'd make it up to you if I could, but I...' Her voice trailed off at the glitter in his eyes.

'Oh, you'll make it up to me all right.' There was a razor-sharp edge to his voice. 'I consoled myself with the thought that one day I'd find you and make you pay, and believe me I shall enjoy every moment of it.' Pushing back his chair with a scraping noise, he added abruptly, 'Let's take a walk.'

She looked up slowly, the tears drying on her cheeks, and shook her head. 'I don't have time to take a walk. I need to get back to town and open the shop. Saturday is one of my busiest days.'

Tane didn't say a word, but his expression confirmed her worst fears. He hadn't the slightest intention of letting her go so easily.

Laura set her teeth. 'I can't stay here. I have a business to run.' Then, her voice growing panicky, she added, 'You can't keep me against my will.'

He smiled nastily. 'Do you want to bet?'

'But you don't understand; I *need* to get back. I have...'

With all her instincts screaming out a warning, Laura stopped abruptly, as shocked as if she'd walked smack into a plate-glass window, as she realised she'd almost mentioned Jamie.

His dark face grim and unyielding, Tane was waiting by the door. Conceding defeat, at least temporarily, she stumbled to her feet and accompanied him out of the house. Feet scrunching, they crossed the gravel apron where his car was parked, and turned left down the quiet country lane.

It was pleasantly warm and sunny, and as they walked Laura's jangled nerves quietened somewhat. The flat marsh countryside was intersected by dykes and reed-fringed waterways, and the air held a salt tang which suggested they weren't too far from the sea. Tane set a brisk pace and they went for several miles without passing more than an occasional farm.

Towards lunchtime the loop they were following took them through Thorncliffe, a hamlet made up of perhaps a dozen dwellings, an old stone church and a seventeenth-century inn.

As they drew level with the Lamb and Flag he broke the silence to ask, 'Would you like to stop for a drink and a bar meal?'

Laura was thirsty rather than hungry, but she answered, 'Yes, that would be nice.'

Apart from one or two locals they had the place to themselves. Sitting in the cool dimness of a low-ceilinged bar, where the sour-apple smell of cider and the sharp scent of geraniums mingled, they ate salad cobs and drank glasses of lager.

Tane's dark profile looked aloof, unapproachable, but, knowing she had to resume the battle some time, Laura remarked with forced casualness, 'I really ought to be at the shop. I can't afford to...'

His sharp glance made the words falter and die on her lips.

After a moment or so she took her courage by the scruff of the neck and tried again from a different angle. 'Marsh House, who does it belong to?'

Sounding remote, he replied, 'It's mine. I bought it two or three years ago.'

Anxious to keep the conversation going, she asked the first thing that came into her head. 'How do you manage? I mean, does someone look after it for you?'

'A Mrs Chapel from the village buys any provisions I may need, and goes in a couple of times a week to do anything that's necessary.'

'Then you've never married?'

He gave her a look that turned the blood in her veins to ice. 'No, I've never married. Did you think it was likely?'

Awkwardly, she said, 'Well, it's been four years.'

'Would you care to guess how I've spent those four long years?'

Inwardly cringing from so much bitterness, Laura shook her head.

'Working sixteen hours a day in order to try and stop myself thinking, while I paid detectives to search for you.'

Unable to look at him, she stared at her hands as he went on, 'During the blackest periods, when I felt the need to get away from people and be on my own, when I couldn't bear the penthouse and I got tired of walking the streets, I'd come here.'

Knowing there was nothing she could say, Laura bit her soft inner lip until she tasted blood.

After a moment, his voice like a whetted knife, he demanded, 'Any more questions?'

Refusing to be intimidated, she lifted her head and met his gaze straightly. 'Yes, quite a few.'

A glimmer of respect in his smoky eyes, he drawled, 'Very well; fire away.'

Taking a deep breath, she asked the thousand-dollar question. 'Why did you bring me to Marsh House?'

His teeth gleamed in a mirthless smile. 'I thought I'd already answered that one.'

'You implied you intended to...to rape me. But I don't believe it.'

He shrugged. 'That's your prerogative. Next question.'

Laura phrased it with care. 'How long do you mean to stay here?'

'I haven't decided exactly; I may take a holiday. It's been over four years since I had one.'

'Tane...' She swallowed, then went on jerkily, 'I *have* to get back to town. I have commitments.'

'Such as a non-existent husband?'

She didn't answer, and he went on, 'Having seen your place, it's quite obvious that you live alone.'

When she stayed stubbornly silent he continued, 'And Perry told me you'd had the shop and the "flat" for nearly a year, and in all that time he'd never seen sight or sign of a husband.'

Driven, she asked, 'Did Perry also tell you that the next quarter's rent is nearly due?' With something approaching desperation, she added, 'If the shop stays closed I won't be able to find it. Then what shall I do?'

'I suggest an appeal to your landlord.'

Recalling Perry's lustful eyes and the way he'd tried to touch her, Laura shuddered with revulsion.

'Do I gather the suggestion isn't altogether welcome?' Tane queried with mock gravity. Only too aware that he was deliberately baiting her, Laura gritted her teeth and said nothing. 'Perhaps if you had a change of landlord?'

Some nuance in his tone made her glance at him sharply, and gave birth to a sudden suspicion. She tried to tell herself he wouldn't go to such lengths, but she knew he would.

Tane smiled grimly, as if reading her thoughts.

Striving for calmness, she said, 'You still haven't told me why you went to see Perry.'

He looked at her, those eyes the exact blue-grey of wood-smoke. 'I wanted to find out about you, about your tenancy.'

'Why? What do you *want*?'

'Complete control. I want you in the palm of my hand.'

His answer was given so casually that for a moment it scarcely sank in. When it did, Laura's blood ran cold.

'To further that end,' Tane went on smoothly, 'I made Perry an offer he was only too happy to accept. As soon as the necessary formalities are completed, the Lulworth building is mine.'

Feeling like a kitten who had received an anticipated, but still unavoidable boot in the midriff, Laura relapsed into silence.

They walked back at a slightly more leisurely pace. By the time they reached the house a chill wind had sprung up, the sun had disappeared behind dark skeins of cloud, and heavy spots of rain were falling.

The kitchen, though packed with modern labour-saving devices, was a big old-fashioned living-kitchen, with a huge fireplace. At Tane's suggestion, Laura looked in the fridge and set about preparing an evening meal while he kindled a fire in the log-cradle standing in the wide stone hearth.

While she worked she was aware that he watched her ceaselessly, and her inner tension mounted until she was close to screaming-point. What did he *really* want? Presumably an outlet, a release, for all the hate that filled him . . . to make her pay—he'd said as much. But what form was that 'payment' to take? Was he trying to break her? To reduce her to a nervous wreck?

Well, she couldn't allow that to happen. She had to be strong, had to survive, for Jamie's sake. The thought of her son had Laura glancing surreptitiously at her watch. It was just after six. Molly might think something was wrong if she didn't make her usual call.

As though in answer to her unspoken prayer, Tane picked up the empty log basket and headed for the door. The instant it closed behind him, Laura hurried through to the living-room and looked around anxiously. Surely there was a phone somewhere? She recalled seeing the wires running from the lane across to the house.

A hurried search drew a blank. Perhaps there was one in the adjacent room, which appeared to serve as a study? The door was standing a trifle ajar. She pushed it open and glanced in. There, on the small leather-topped table, was a cream phone and, alongside it, the telephone directory.

Quickly she picked up the receiver and dialled Molly's number, holding her breath until the familiar voice, with its edge of brogue, answered.

Having gone through the nightly routine, Laura said quickly, 'One other thing. I can't go into details now, but something's come up and I...I don't know whether I'll be able to get to you tomorrow.'

'You're sure you're all right?' Molly demanded.

'Yes, quite all right,' Laura said firmly. 'There's no need to worry. I'll give you a ring when I can...' A movement caught her eye and she stopped speaking abruptly.

Tane was standing in the doorway.

Trying not to look guilty, she replaced the receiver.

'Who were you calling?' Beneath the polite interest, his voice was diamond-hard.

'Just a friend,' Laura said as evenly as possible.

'A man?'

'A woman. She was expecting me to ring...I thought if I didn't she might wonder...'

In two strides he was by her side, his fingers closing around her wrist like a steel trap. 'Suppose you tell me the truth.'

'That was the truth.'

His grip tightened until she winced but, lifting her head, she looked him in the eye. 'Of course if you *want* me to lie and say it was a man...'

He made a small sound of fury in his throat, and she tensed herself for an explosion. But after a nerve-racking second or two he released her wrist, and indicated that she should precede him back to the kitchen.

She did so, her heart banging against her ribs, convinced it was only a temporary reprieve.

CHAPTER FOUR

SUMMONING all her reserves of will-power, Laura gradually forced herself to relax. The exercise in self-control worked well, and she even managed to make small talk while she finished cooking the chicken Kiev and they ate.

Tane answered in the same vein, but he watched her with piercing eyes, as if both annoyed and baffled by her apparent serenity.

Only when she'd cleared away and stacked the dirty crockery in the dishwasher did a sudden ripple of alarm spoil her surface calm. There was a whole evening to be got through, not to mention the coming night. After lingering for as long as possible over the few remaining tasks, she crossed to the hearth, where the fire was blazing merrily, and took a seat in an old rocking-chair.

Tane, who had been sitting on the chintz-covered settee staring morosely into the leaping flames, looked up.

Meeting those smoky eyes made her feel as if her heart was being squeezed in a vice. Her chest hurt and she found it difficult to draw air into her lungs. Tearing her gaze away, she said with determined composure, 'Are there any cards? We could have a game of Progress.'

'Progress?'

She caught, and ignored, the flicker of surprise. 'If you don't know how to play it, I'll teach you,' she offered.

He gave her a look which she couldn't decipher, and replied drily, 'Oh, *I* know how to play it. I wasn't aware you did.'

David had taught her. She'd played it often with him when he'd needed something to take his mind off the worsening pain.

Rising to his feet, Tane opened a drawer in the dresser and, producing a pack of cards, pulled a low table between them. 'Would you like to play the advantage rule?' he asked.

Coolly, she said, 'I don't think that will be necessary.'

He shrugged. 'On your own head be it.'

It was a fast, complicated game which demanded both skill and concentration. When Laura won the first round, Tane's conscious look of superiority faded. He won the second by the skin of his teeth, and she the third, easily.

'Another?' she enquired innocently. After surveying her through narrowed eyes, he agreed.

She won all three rounds.

He was so staggered, almost outraged, that her dimples appeared. 'How the devil did you manage that?' he demanded.

Smugly, she answered, 'I cheat.'

After an incredulous second he threw back his head and laughed aloud.

All at once she was looking at the old Tane, his face alight with amusement and charm. His laughter was so infectious that she found herself laughing with him, the intervening years wiped away as if they'd never been. Then in a split second the mirth was gone and he was gazing at her, his face full of naked emotion. Desire, anger, pain, and hunger, all mingled.

Laura's throat went dry and tight and the blood began to race through her veins. He got up and, hands on her shoulders, forced her to her feet, holding her as if it pleased him to hurt her.

Eyes huge in the heart-shaped face, she tilted back her head to look at him. As though that was an invitation, he bent to kiss her, but she turned sharply away and his lips brushed chastely across her cheek.

Catching hold of her chin, he wrenched it round. In a tortured voice he muttered, 'Kiss me... kiss me, damn you! I've waited so long.'

When she kept quite still, unresponsive as marble, mutely resisting both his domination and his pleas, he said with driving anger, 'You stand there so *unmoved*. Have you any idea what you did to me? How you spoilt me for every other woman...?

'Oh, I don't mean I've been completely celibate for over four years, but for months at a time I lived like a monk. Night after night I lay unable to sleep. When I couldn't stand it any longer I bought myself a succession of mistresses to assuage a physical need I couldn't totally sublimate.

'I never *wanted* or cared about any of them. I only *used* them.' There was bitterness and self-contempt in his voice. 'But even kept women have their pride. Though they put up with it, none of them liked being treated as whores, and it made me hate and despise myself as well as them.'

Unbearably moved, Laura whispered, 'Oh, Tane, I...'

He ran his fingers into her silky hair, holding her head still while his mouth swooped, stopping her words, claiming hers with a savage craving that crushed any attempt at opposition. Her own heartbeat thundered in her ears as he rained kisses on her face, her closed eyelids, her temples, her throat, before his mouth closed over hers once more.

The way someone drowning caught at a straw, she tried desperately to keep a grasp on her feelings, some hold on sanity, but it was all dark chaos and confusion, overwhelming as being swept away by a tidal wave.

Hardly knowing how she got there, Laura found herself lying on the rug in front of the hearth, naked to the waist, the fine gold chain around her neck gleaming in the firelight.

Tane was beside her, his hands on her breasts, stroking, teasing, stimulating. Then his mouth took the place of his fingers, wringing from her little moans and gasps and shudders she was unable to prevent.

His hand moved up to the smoothness of her inner thigh to rest on the delicate silk and lace that was her only protection. The alternating pressure of his warm palm combined with his sweet, hungry suckling made her writhe and whimper and set up such a longing, a need, that she ached for him.

It was only when her body was utterly abandoned, lost in a flood of sensations, that her mind fought its way to the surface. She wanted him to make love to her... but it wasn't love that impelled him, it was lust. Lust and anger and hatred. A deadly combination.

No, she couldn't allow this to happen.

Terribly afraid that she'd left it too late, she began to struggle, but he held her easily, using the weight of his body to keep her where he wanted her, his hand to prove his dominance.

Still she resisted fiercely. 'No, no... leave me alone.'

Breathing as if he'd run too far, too fast, he advised, 'Don't waste your energy fighting me. You'll need it. I'm going to have you in my bed, and keep you there until I'm sated and you're begging for mercy, if it takes a year.'

Shock made Laura feel as though she'd just been tossed into a whirlpool. Almost incoherent, hardly aware of what she was saying, she babbled, 'Please, oh, please, Tane... don't make me stay. I have to get back. I have to see Jamie...'

Suddenly his weight lifted, her upper arms were seized, and she was jerked into a sitting position. 'Jamie?' Tane's voice was quiet, lethal. 'Who's Jamie? Is he the one you sneaked away to phone?'

Her wits totally swamped, she just stared at him.

He repeated the question, his fingers tightening painfully on her soft flesh. She gave a little murmur of protest. With a kind of raging calm, he said, 'I mean to have an answer if I have to beat it out of you.'

A chill ran over her and she shivered in his hands.

He looked at her pinched face, at the gooseflesh that roughened the creamy skin and, pulling her to her feet, he said harshly, 'You'd better get dressed.'

Her hands were shaking so badly that, by the time she'd dragged on her clothes, he'd put a couple of logs on the fire and poured them each a brandy. Sinking into the rocking-chair, she sipped the amber spirit, the glass chinking against her teeth as she tried to hold it steady.

It had grown much darker and a blustery wind was hurling handfuls of rain against the leaded panes. The early gloaming, the crackling logs, would have made the atmosphere relaxed and cosy if it hadn't been for the almost tangible strain in the air.

Tane stood by the hearth, tall and brooding, firelight flickering on the hard lines of his handsome face, and making his eyes gleam between the thick, dark lashes. His pose was indolent, but Laura could sense a core of tension like a tightly coiled spring inside him. He put her in mind of some sleek jungle animal poised to make a kill.

Trying not to look at him, Laura drank her brandy slowly and did her utmost to regain some semblance of composure. When her glass was empty she placed it on the nearby table—her movement making the gold ring on her third finger shine—and braced herself for what was to come.

Unexpectedly, he reached out and lifted her hand. Before she'd tumbled to what he was about, he had taken the ring from her finger and slipped it into his pocket.

Her deep blue eyes sparkling angrily, she started up. 'How dare you? Give me back my ring!'

He merely took her shoulders and pressed her down into her seat with contemptuous ease. She stared at him resentfully, nursing her bare left hand as if he'd wounded it.

Leaning against the stone mantel, he said insolently, 'I might let you have it back when you tell me the real reason you're wearing it. You know as well as I do you have no husband.'

The remaining colour drained from her face and she bit her lip hard. After a moment she said stiffly, 'As a matter of fact you're right.'

Something that could have been relief flashed briefly in Tane's eyes, and she realised he hadn't been nearly as confident as he'd sounded.

He moved a log with the toe of his shoe, sending up a shower of bright, crackling sparks, before continuing, 'That brings us to Jamie. How does *he* fit into your life?' Looking at her tight lips, the stubborn set of her jaw, he added, 'I've been very patient, but now I want some answers.'

'I won't be *interrogated*,' she retorted fiercely.

'All right, I'll leave it to you to tell me what happened during the time we were apart. Start with the night you ran out on me, and tell me everything.'

'Very well.' She took up the gauntlet. He wanted to know, so he *should* know. But not *everything*...

She had preferred not to remember the anguish, the black nights and bleak dawns when she'd been enmeshed in a bitter hopelessness it had taken her years to free herself from. But now, gazing into the heart of the fire, watching the orange and blue flames licking round the logs, she deliberately sent her thoughts back to the past.

After a moment or two, in a voice devoid of emotion, but at the same time pulling no punches, she told him how despair for the future had made her decide to pack her cases and leave. 'At first I didn't know where to run to, I——'

'Just a minute,' Tane said in a queer, wrenched voice. 'Are you trying to tell me you left because you loved me too much to stay and chance hurting me *more*?'

'That's exactly what I'm trying to tell you.'

'I don't believe you.'

She had hoped that he would believe her, hoped that the knowledge would alleviate some of his pain. Quietly, she said, 'I can't *make* you believe me. All the same, it's the truth.'

After what seemed to be an endless pause, he ordered, 'Go on.'

A succession of shudders running through her, Laura went on to tell him about her arrival at David's flat, and how desolate she'd been during the following days.

'But when I realised how much it upset him to see me so low, I pulled myself together and began to pick up the threads again.

'David had been having health problems for some time, and he needed to go as an out-patient to Dale End hospital. It was a long, tiring journey, so we decided to move closer.'

That hadn't been the sole reason for the move, and a quick glance at Tane's face showed he knew quite well what the other consideration had been.

She went on, 'We were lucky enough to find a furnished flat to let——'

'Did he pay all the rent?' Tane broke in.

Without looking at him, she was aware that he was seething with futile anger and something that could have been jealousy.

'No,' she answered truthfully. 'Though the flat was smaller than David's previous one, it was more expensive, so I took a temporary job in a coffee bar to help with finances...'

'Joe's' had been hot and steamy, and she'd been on her feet all day. Feeling ill and nauseated, it had taken every iota of will-power to keep her going. She'd been there when the result of her pregnancy test had come through. But even before that she'd been sure.

The first month, still in an emotional maelstrom, she hadn't given it a thought. By the second month she was feeling sick every morning with monotonous regularity, and there was no need for thought.

She had known it must have happened that very first night at the Little Mermaid, the night Tane had asked her to marry him, and her ardent response had had the same effect as dropping a lighted match into a pool of petrol. After that he had been careful to take precautions.

Unwilling to worry David, to add to his problems, she had put off telling him she was pregnant. But one morning, when he'd come down to breakfast and discovered her hanging on to the bathroom sink, white-faced and queasy, he'd said bluntly, 'You're having a baby, aren't you?'

She'd nodded.

He'd looked at her, a bleak expression in his hazel eyes. 'When are you going to tell him?'

Horror-stricken, she'd cried, 'I'm not going to tell him! He wouldn't want to know. He...he hates children.'

'It's his responsibility. The very least he can do is help support it.'

'No, it's *my* responsibility. I don't want him to know.'

Pulling her into his arms, David had held her close. 'Then I'll take care of you. We'll be married as soon as possible.'

He'd wanted her to give up working, but knowing how much they needed the money she had insisted on keeping her job, at least for the time being.

Their register office wedding was only ten days away when David had to go to Dale End for the results of his latest batch of tests. That night as they ate their evening meal she asked him about them. He was so evasive that she became uneasy, suspicious.

When the dishes had been washed and they were sitting in their shabby little lounge, she was about to broach the subject again when he said with care, 'I've been thinking. Perhaps our getting married is a mistake. Maybe you'd be better off striking out on your own.'

She turned to him and, taking his thin, fair face between her palms, asked, 'What is it, love? What's the matter?'

Finally, after much badgering, he'd told her, ending, 'The doctor says it's pernicious and fast-moving. I'll be in hospital in a matter of months, and dead inside two years.'

'Oh, no!' she cried. 'How can he say that?'

'I insisted that he tell me the truth without wrapping it up.'

'No, I mean, how can he be sure? They're finding new treatments, new cures, almost every day. There could be a breakthrough...'

'Sweetheart——' he took her hand and held it tightly '—don't think I haven't told myself all that. But we both know it's unlikely, to say the least. That's why I think it might be better to forget about getting married.'

So he was afraid he was going to be an additional burden to her.

'I don't want to forget about it,' she said. 'I need you. We need each other.'

'But——'

She put a slim, strong hand over his mouth. 'No buts. I want a ring on my finger and my baby to have a name.' Then, with spirit, 'If you try to back out now I'll swear it's yours and sue you for breach of promise.'

He'd smiled then and said, 'Bless you, my darling...'

Laura became aware that Tane was waiting, watching the play of emotions over her face.

Brusquely, he said, 'You were working in a coffee bar... So what happened then? Did your precious David make you his mistress?'

'No,' she answered steadily, 'he made me his wife. I'm Mrs David James Belmont.'

She heard the hiss of Tane's indrawn breath. Tipped off balance he accused thickly, 'You're lying.'

'Why should I lie about it?'

'You once told me you wouldn't marry him. You said there was no passion there.'

She laughed bitterly. 'I'd had enough of passion. Look where it got me.'

'You wouldn't marry me because you wanted a family, then you go and take a sickly husband who hasn't given you any children.'

Laura lifted her chin, her face full of delicate strength. 'Oh, but he has. You wanted to know how Jamie fitted into my life. Well, I'll tell you. He's my son.'

Tane's face whitened beneath the tan as if her words were rocks she'd hit him with. 'How can I believe you? A short time ago you agreed you hadn't a husband.'

'David died a year ago,' she said quietly.

'I'm sorry,' Tane muttered. 'That must have been rough on you.'

'He was a fine man. Though he knew he was dying, he never once lost his courage, and right until the end he put me and Jamie first.

'I kept him at home as long as possible, but when he had to go into hospital we went to see him every day. Even when he was too ill to lift his head, his eyes used to light up when he saw us.'

Abruptly Tane walked to the window and stood staring out into the semi-darkness, his broad back to the room. After a long silence he asked, 'What about the boy?'

'I have to have him looked after,' she answered regretfully. 'There's no way I can keep him with me at the shop. Luckily he's a good, sunny-natured child, and Molly says he's quite happy.'

Turning away from the window, Tane resumed his stance by the fire. His face was still paler than normal and there was a tightness about his mouth, but his tone was casual as he queried, 'Where does this Molly live?'

Purposely vague, Laura answered, 'In Ealing.'

'Is she some distant relative?'

'No. I met her at the hospital. She used to visit John— her husband—each day, and we became friends. Her children and grandchildren are in various corners of the globe, so when John died she was alone.

'Molly's very fond of children, and it was she who suggested looking after Jamie for me.'

Frowning a little, Tane commented, 'It can't be good for a young child to spend all his time with an elderly woman who's lonely and depressed.'

'He doesn't spend all his time with her,' Laura said, 'he goes to a privately run play-school each morning. In any case, Molly is neither lonely nor depressed. She has too much spirit, not to mention a spiky sense of humour and a nice turn of phrase.

'She's lived here most of her life, but she comes from Ireland. For years she was a kindergarten teacher, so I've no real worries about Jamie. It's just that, with only seeing him one day a week, I'm missing so much of his childhood...' The prick of tears behind her eyes stopped her speaking abruptly.

'So it was Molly you rang tonight.'

Though it was a statement rather than a question, Laura nodded. Then, suddenly feeling unutterably weary, she said, 'I'd like to go to bed.'

'Is that an invitation?' he asked.

'No,' she answered shortly.

He sighed. 'Tell me something, my torment... *is* there a man in your life?'

'That's none of your business,' she retorted.

He gave her a long, half-veiled look, the thick curly lashes hiding the expression in his blue-grey eyes. 'I'm making it my business. I don't believe there's been anyone since your... since Belmont died.'

Laura stared at him for a moment, her heart flailing around like a wounded bird, then asked wearily, 'Does it matter?'

'Perhaps not. There's no way of altering what's past.' He sounded grim, defeated.

When Laura reached the stairs she found herself almost too tired to climb them, and Tane put an arm around her waist and helped her. At her bedroom door he lifted her chin and dropped a swift, hard kiss on her lips before walking away.

Left to herself, she pulled off her clothes, fell into bed, and slept almost as soon as her head hit the pillow.

Next morning, she awoke to complete and immediate remembrance, and lay in the quiet room, her mind seething with troubled thoughts. Even though he didn't know the full truth, the fact that she had been married and borne a child had undoubtedly been a great shock to Tane.

In telling him, she had hoped, indeed half *expected* that, when he realised the gulf which divided them, it would alter his thinking, his intentions, make him decide to withdraw from her life and leave her alone.

Maybe, now he'd had a chance to assimilate it, it *would*. He himself had made the point that it was impossible to alter what was past.

Her heart ached for him. He was so bitter and warped, all the love he'd once felt turned to hate and a strange, tortured desire that amounted almost to an obsession. An obsession that, uncontrolled, could end up destroying both of them...

Laura jumped violently as, without warning, the door opened and Tane strolled in. He looked dangerously attractive in grey trousers that hugged his lean hips, and a white shirt unbuttoned to show the tanned column of his throat and the beginning of the sprinkling of crisp dark hair on his chest.

He put the oval tray he was carrying down on the bedside table, and, when she'd struggled into a sitting position, plumped up the pillows behind her. Cool and unruffled, far removed from the racked, obsessed man of her thoughts, he smiled at her.

'Sleep well?' he asked.

'Yes, thank you.' Her voice was husky.

It was at that point she realised he was studying her with an appreciative gleam in his smoky eyes, a gleam that reminded her that the silk and lace slip she'd slept in was almost transparent. She made an awkward movement to cover herself with the sheet.

He sighed theatrically, then, his smile distinctly mocking, murmured, 'Never mind, I have excellent recall. I know how silky and flawless your skin is, how soft and heavy your breasts feel weighed in my hands, how the dusky pink——'

'Stop it!' she cried in a strangled voice, only too aware of the effect his words were having on her.

'Sorry,' he said mendaciously. 'Am I upsetting you?'

Exaggeratedly careful not to disturb the sheet, he placed the tray across her knees. It was daintily set with orange juice, a boiled egg, toast and marmalade, a pot of coffee, and two china cups. A single beautiful red rose lay by her plate. With a curious mingling of pleasure and pain, Laura picked it up to inhale its perfume.

The first morning after she'd moved into his penthouse he'd brought her such a tray. That time the rose had been a perfect, long-stemmed specimen from a florist. This time it was a garden flower, with morning dew still glistening on its velvet petals, and sharp thorns.

About to replace it, she gave a little exclamation as one of the thorns pierced her flesh.

Tane picked up her hand and looked at the bright drop of blood welling from the pad of her index finger. Before she could guess his intention, he put her fingertip in his mouth, sucking gently.

Laura gave a stifled gasp as desire kicked in her abdomen. His eyes met hers, his coolly ironic gaze telling her he knew exactly what effect he was having on her. Pulling her hand free, she hastily picked up the glass of orange juice.

'Steady,' he said, gently derisive. 'We don't want it spilt all over the counterpane.'

Sitting down on the edge of the bed, facing her, he helped himself to a piece of golden toast, and buttered it while she tapped the shell of a brown speckled egg with the bowl of her spoon.

She'd done the same thing on the previous occasion, and he'd teased her about her dainty ways, saying it was much quicker and more efficient to cut off the top with a knife. While they'd wrangled amicably over the merits of the different methods, she'd spoon-fed him the top off her egg.

Now she looked up at him slowly, and, as if under a spell, offered this one to him.

He ate it, and smiled into her eyes.

Recalling that last time, when they had pushed aside the tray and ended up back in bed making long, delectable love, she blushed as red as the rose.

His response was a soft, satisfied laugh.

Holding on to her tattered composure as best she could, she looked down at her plate and, though her appetite had fled, concentrated on eating.

When she'd swallowed the last bite of her toast and licked a sliver of marmalade from her finger with a pink tongue, he poured coffee for them both and remarked,

'As it's Sunday I thought you might like to go back to town and spend the afternoon with your son.'

'Oh, *yes*, I——' She came to an abrupt halt. 'Do you mean I'm free to leave, or...?'

'I mean I'll be very happy to take you.'

Laura sipped her coffee, trying to hide her sudden concern and apprehension. The very last thing she wanted was for Tane to know exactly where Molly and Jamie lived, to invade her life any further; but his brain was razor-sharp, and too strong a reaction might make him wonder...

Casually, she said, 'Once I'm back in town, it's quite quick and easy to get a bus.'

Equally casually, he replied, 'Surely it's even quicker and easier by car?'

Did he intend to just drop her there? Or was he planning to pick her up again afterwards and carry on this war of attrition?

Removing all doubt as to what his intentions were, he remarked, 'Molly seems to be quite a character. I'd rather like to meet her.' Adding, 'Afterwards we'll have dinner at my place.'

Having waited for Laura to finish her coffee and re-place the cup, he picked up the tray and made his way downstairs, leaving her in a state bordering on panic. Now what was she to do?

She did her best to think rationally. What might the consequences be if Tane found out that Jamie was *his* son?

Given his dislike of children, such a discovery could be all that was needed to make him walk out of her life for good, and leave her in comparative peace.

But somehow she didn't think so.

Even though he hated her, she couldn't see him leaving her to support his child when he knew of her financial difficulties.

One thing was certain, however: the knowledge that the boy was his would give him an intolerable hold over her. Though Jamie couldn't be said to be the image of his father, they were sufficiently alike to make any meeting a very real risk. So somehow, without arousing Tane's suspicions, she had to prevent him seeing the child.

Without arousing Tane's suspicions. There, in a nut-shell, was the real problem. If it hadn't been for that proviso she could have just flatly refused to tell him where Molly lived. As it was...

Jumping out of bed, she opened the door, and, having peered out cautiously, crept downstairs. Several times she paused, her heart in her mouth, as the old wooden treads creaked loudly. In bare feet she padded into the study and picked up the phone.

Molly answered almost immediately. 'Yes, who is it?'

Speaking just above a whisper, Laura said, 'It's me... Listen, this is urgent. Someone is bringing me over to see Jamie, but I want you to get him out of the house on some pretext or other, and *keep* him out. I can't explain now, but I——'

From the corner of her eye she saw the door move, and started to put the receiver down. When Tane strolled in, her hand was still on it.

Her brain working like lightning, she said a shade breathlessly, 'Oh, I was just going to give Molly a ring and tell her we'd be over later today.'

He looked at her, his gaze clear and coolly perceptive. 'I rather thought this Sunday visit was a standing arrangement.'

'It is, but I—I usually go alone.'

'Does it make any difference whether you're alone or not?'

'I suppose not.'

Seeing his eyes move with all male enjoyment down the length of her figure in the see-through slip, Laura turned hastily away, her colour rising. 'I'd better go and get ready.'

Her emotions a mixture of relief that she'd got away with it, embarrassment at being caught half naked, and disappointment at the thought of not seeing Jamie, she escaped upstairs.

Molly was no fool. Though she might be surprised, she would somehow contrive to do as she'd been asked, and hopefully without giving Tane cause to wonder or suspect anything.

CHAPTER FIVE

As soon as Laura was ready, they went out to the car. Tane, who had put on a tie and jacket, drove in silence. Her thoughts disquieting, she glanced at him from time to time, but his face remained remote, austere.

It was a cold, windy day, with puffs of grey cloud being driven across the leaden sky like smoke signals. About twelve-thirty they stopped at a pub for a bar snack. Not wanting to get to Molly's too soon, Laura lingered over her salad, spinning out the minutes until Tane remarked, 'I imagined you'd be in more of a hurry to see your son.'

Searching for an excuse, she said, 'I was just thinking, it's bound to seem odd if I turn up with a strange man, and not wearing my wedding-ring.'

Just for an instant, an expression of real pain crossed Tane's face, then it was gone, masked by a grim determination which made Laura feel uneasy.

Quietly but implacably, he said, 'I can't allow you to go on wearing another man's ring. Anyway, you're not a married woman any longer, you're a widow. If you need to explain me to Molly, put this on and tell her I'm your fiancé.' He felt in his pocket, flicked open a blue leather box, and held it out.

Making no attempt to take it, she sat as if turned to ivory, staring at the huge diamond solitaire which was achingly familiar, and which had looked so beautiful on her slim, long-fingered hand.

'Well?' he asked harshly.

Mutely she shook her head.

He snapped shut the box and returned it to his pocket.

She'd half expected him to force the issue, to put it on her finger and insist on her wearing it. The fact that he hadn't left her with a strange feeling of mingled reprieve and desolation.

Why had he kept the ring? she wondered. When a love-affair crumbled, a relationship fell apart, wouldn't most men have got rid of it, put the whole sorry mess behind them and found consolation in the arms of some other woman? That was what she had expected Tane to do.

She had never thought of the break-up having such a devastating effect on him, never imagined his feelings would go so deep. Neither had she dreamt of him becoming so bitter, and brooding, blaming *her*. She hadn't blamed *him*, only fate for making them so far apart in their thinking and what they wanted and needed from life.

He had accused her of running out on him, but, if she'd stayed and they'd talked further, even if he'd told her about his childhood, would it have made any difference?

As he himself had said, *understanding* didn't necessarily provide an answer, a solution. But, if she'd stayed, could they have possibly ameliorated their differences?

If she'd stayed...

The question was academic, but, if she *had* stayed only to discover she was already pregnant, where would that have left them?

It was nearly three o'clock by the time the white Mercedes was drawing up outside Molly's spacious, spick-and-span bungalow. With elaborate courtesy, Tane opened the green painted gate and escorted Laura up the narrow, paved path which ran between colourful flower-beds. Seeing the spotless net curtains twitch, she smiled to herself.

His hand had scarcely touched the knocker when the door opened with a suddenness that made him blink, and a short, neatly dressed woman popped up in the doorway like a pink-cheeked Jill-in-the-box.

'Come in, come in, the pair of you.' Then to Laura, 'To be sure, I thought you'd never get here!'

She led them across the wide passage, which ran from end to end of the bungalow, and into a pleasant sitting-room with a lived-in, homely feel to it. Eschewing any attempt at explanations, Laura said simply, 'Molly, this is Tane Carlson...Tane, Molly Seaton.'

Molly had a lissom figure with a waistline any girl might have envied. Crisp grey hair curled around a puckish face which was clear and unlined. Her teeth were good, her nose an upturned blob, her eyes, speckled green as opals, held more than a touch of devilment. From her five feet nothing she looked up to Tane's six feet plus, and held out her hand with an impish grin.

He took it and smiled back, his good-looking face full of charm and genuine warmth. 'How do you do, Mrs Seaton?'

She batted her pale, stubby lashes at him shamelessly. 'Most people call me Molly.'

Head on one side, he considered her. '"Molly, oh, Molly, as trim as she's pretty, a neat girl, a sweet girl, who steals the boys' hearts..."'

Molly eyed him back, and said tartly, 'Sure there's one here who doesn't need to kiss the Blarney stone.' But all the same she was pleased. 'Now, then, take off your things and sit yourselves down.' She indicated a settee drawn up cosily to a log-effect gas fire.

Tane helped Laura off with her coat before removing his own jacket. He loomed large and very masculine, out of place in a room full of feminine fripperies.

While Molly relieved him of the garments, as unobtrusively as possible Laura moved to take a seat in one of the armchairs. He gave her a quizzical look which showed he appreciated the manoeuvre, and sat down directly opposite, making her wonder if she'd made the right choice after all. She knew by now that he could destroy her composure, make her grow hot and fidgety, just by looking at her.

Molly bustled back and sat herself down on the settee beside Tane. Eyeing the elegant skirt and blouse that, seeing nothing else for it, Laura had reluctantly donned, she exclaimed admiringly, 'My, but aren't you just the cat's whiskers! And haven't I been telling you it was high time you treated yourself to something nice?'

Laura managed a smile, then, bracing herself, seized the bull by the horns and asked brightly, 'Where's Jamie?'

Suddenly the air was threaded with tension.

'I'm sorry, pet,' Molly said, 'but I've let him go out.'

'That's a pity,' Tane remarked in his low-pitched, attractive voice. 'I'm sure Laura will be most disappointed.'

Was there a subtle sarcasm in his last words? Laura wondered. Or was it merely her guilty conscience?

Molly took up his challenge without turning a hair. 'Well, when it got to two o'clock I made certain Herself wasn't coming...'

Tane turned to Laura and clicked his tongue. 'Perhaps you *should* have rung to say we were coming, after all.' Then he gave Molly a glinting smile and said, 'I'm sorry, do go on.'

Unruffled, she went on, 'And Anne Masters had asked if the bairn could go to their Mark's birthday party.'

'Then he'll be home before we leave?' Tane suggested smoothly. 'Children's parties don't usually go on too late.'

'No, that he won't,' Molly said positively.

'Oh?' Tane lifted a dark brow.

Her speckled green eyes wide and guileless, she explained, 'You see, they live a little way away and he's staying the night. Both the bairns go to the same play-school, so Anne will take them in tomorrow morning, and I'll pick Jamie up from there at lunchtime.'

'Nicely arranged,' Tane congratulated her.

'Yes, I thought so,' she agreed complacently.

Laura had listened to this little exchange with a kind of fearful fascination, unable to decide if Tane actually suspected Molly of subterfuge. Whether he did or not, his last words had sounded as if he was saluting a worthy opponent.

Perhaps he would suggest leaving now? she thought hopefully. He'd met Molly, and found Jamie wouldn't be back...

But, stretching his long legs with graceful indolence, he snapped the threads of tension, and set the ball of social conversation rolling by asking, 'Who does your garden for you? It's very nicely kept.'

'John, my husband, used to do it until he died last year. Now I take care of it myself.'

'You must miss him.'

'So I do. Though Himself wasn't much of a gardener, the Lord love him, and even less of a mechanic. He once mended the lawn-mower...' There was a pregnant pause while she waited for the feed question.

Tane obliged. 'And did it work?'

'Oh, yes, it *worked*, but only if you *pulled* it.'

'An unusual and—er—talented man,' Tane observed, his voice grave, but his eyes crinkling into laughter-lines at the corners as he smiled.

'He was the only male my mother had no apparent effect on. Sometimes I think that's why I married him.'

'I take it your mother was a formidable lady?'

'She only had to *look* at any boyfriend I took home to make him turn pale and stutter. But Himself was always pasty, and he had a permanent stammer...'

Any other time Laura would have been highly amused by this double act, but now, with so much on her mind, she sat quiet and unsmiling.

As the afternoon wore on it became increasingly plain that, given a handsome, fascinating man to play verbal games with, Molly was in her element. Tane too seemed to be enjoying the encounter. He looked easy and relaxed, well entertained.

Nevertheless it came as a distinct relief to Laura when Molly said, 'Now, then, will I be getting a bite of tea ready?'

'I'll help,' Laura offered, wanting to have a private word with the older woman. But to her chagrin Tane rose to his feet as well. Damn his smoky eyes! she thought wrathfully, as he followed them into the sparkling blue and white kitchen.

Laura cut and buttered home-baked bread while Molly, slicing cucumber as though she were guillotining her enemies, rattled on, 'And I've a nice, tasty bit of ham...' she paused to smack Tane's fingers as he filched a piece of cucumber '...though these days they cut it so thin it looks like a blush on the bread, so it does...'

They had eaten their way through an ample spread, and were on their second cup of tea when, without warning, Tane asked, 'How old is Jamie?'

'Going on for three and a half,' Molly answered.

At exactly the same instant Laura found her tongue and said, 'He's just turned three.'

'When's his birthday?' Tane's question sounded idle, but the muscles of his lean face looked taut beneath the tan.

'The sixth of June,' Laura supplied hastily.

'Surely he's a bit on the young side for play-school?' Tane commented.

'Not a bit of it,' Molly broke in. 'He's bright and intelligent, very forward for his age, and he can talk the hind leg off a donkey.

'To be sure, the bairn's one of those lucky children who seem to have been born feeling at home in the world. Now my youngest grandson . . .'

Another hour went by before, having helped with the dishes, Tane showed any sign of being ready to leave.

Laura knew Molly must be wondering about that panicky phone call, and why she'd lied about Jamie's birthday, but the older woman gave no indication of it as, still talking nineteen to the dozen, she accompanied them to the gate and waved them off.

It had started to rain and blow harder, and the wet streets, looking like black, shiny liquorice, were almost deserted on this dismal, early Sunday evening.

Realising they were heading into the centre of town, and knowing she must make a stand, Laura stated as calmly as possible, 'I'd like to go home.'

'We are going home,' Tane replied, his clear-cut profile set and uncompromising as he looked steadily through the windscreen.

'*My* home,' she insisted.

He gave a short, mirthless laugh. 'Surely you don't call that dingy back room *home*?'

Levelly, she said, 'It's the only home I have. Tane, *please*, I need to open the shop tomorrow. I've a child to support.' When he showed no sign of having heard, she said more forcefully, '*I want to go home!*'

'I've already told you, it isn't what *you* want that counts.'

'You've no right to treat me this way!' she cried.

'If we're talking about *rights* ...'

Uncertain of exactly what he meant, she froze into silence.

When they reached Hunwick Court, Tane tossed one of the garage attendants his car keys, and hurried Laura into the lift. Inside his penthouse, he helped her off with her coat and asked, 'Would you like a drink?'

Shaking her head, she sank into one of the low armchairs. The apartment, which held such bitter-sweet memories of glowing happiness and final despair, was the same, yet not the same. The brown suite had been replaced by a gold corded velvet, and the walls were done in sea colours of green and grey and aquamarine.

She hadn't wanted to come here. But, as Tane had been at pains to point out, it was what *he* wanted that counted. Dear God, where would it all end?

The strain was beginning to tell, and all at once she felt close to breaking-point. Something tight and restricting gripped her chest, and her heart danced hollowly against her ribs.

But he wasn't about to beat or torture her. It was mental pressure, a war of nerves, and he could only break her if she *allowed* him to.

'What does that gallant little lift of the chin signify?' he queried mockingly. 'Does it mean you intend to go on fighting me?'

'I don't want to fight you. I don't want to fight anyone,' she told him with a kind of pathetic dignity. 'All I want is to be left in peace to live my own life.'

'With a failing business and a child to support, it can't be an easy life.'

Woodenly, she stated, 'I can manage.'

When she said nothing further, Tane ordered abruptly, 'Tell me about Jamie.'

She tugged at the gold chain. 'He's a friendly child, sunny-natured and amenable, but, like most children, he can be a little demon at times.'

'Who does he take after? Does he look like you?'

With no time to think, she spoke the exact truth. 'Not really. He's more like his father.'

Then, afraid of where Tane's questions were leading, and deciding to work on the premise that attack was the best means of defence, she added sharply, 'For someone who hates children you're showing a great deal of interest in Jamie.'

A shadow crossed Tane's face. 'I don't hate children,' he denied.

'You said you didn't intend to have any,' she persisted.

A white line appeared around his mouth. 'That doesn't mean I hate them.'

Throwing caution to the winds, she lashed out at him. 'So what does it mean? That you want to be a playboy all your life? That you're too selfish to allow your peaceful routine to be disturbed? That you haven't the confidence, the *guts*, to become a father?'

For a moment she thought she'd pushed him too far. He towered over her, his face livid, his hands clenching and unclenching. Then he swung on his heel and walked to the window. Leaning forward, he rested his forehead against the glass, his breath misting the pane.

There was such anguish and despair in his attitude that she was unable to bear it. Going over to him, she tentatively touched his arm. She could have been touching a statue. Glancing up at his face, she saw that his eyes were closed and there was a pulse throbbing in his temple.

'Tane...' When he didn't answer she took the hand that was clenched into a fist. Making incoherent little murmurs of consolation and endearment, she straightened his fingers, kissing each one, much as she would have done with Jamie, before holding the palm to her cheek.

His eyes flew open and he stood for a moment, appearing almost dazed, his breath coming in harsh rasps as though he'd just run a race.

'I'm sorry,' she whispered. 'Oh, Tane, I'm sorry.'

Snatching his hand away as if it were burnt, he ordered hoarsely, 'Go on, get to bed. In my present mood you may not be safe if you stay.'

She shook her head. 'I don't want to leave you like this.'

With swift urgency he said, 'Then don't leave me... Ah, that widens your eyes and makes you back off.'

'I'm sorry,' she muttered helplessly. 'And even more sorry for what I said.'

'Don't be sorry about that. You're quite right—at least about not having the guts to become a father... Shall I tell you about my childhood?'

Though in the past they'd talked a great deal, sometimes far into the night, he'd never said anything about his early life.

'I wish you would,' she said simply, and thought how shattered he looked, his face set in lines of pain, his eyes dark with weariness and self-contempt.

Taking the initiative, Laura went over to the drinks cabinet, and poured him a brandy. She pushed the goblet into his hand, then sat down again and waited for him to go on, certain in her own mind that what he was going to say would help her to understand why he was as he was.

He tossed back the neat spirit and stood looking through the window, where trickles of rain were running down the glass like tears. Just when Laura began to think he'd changed his mind and decided to remain silent, he said, 'You once remarked that my name was an unusual one. Perhaps it is.

'I was named after a Maori god. Well named,' he went on bitterly. 'In Maori legend Tane was the second son of Papa-Tu-Anuku, the earth mother, and Rangi, the sky father. These two loved each other so much that they always clung together in a passionate embrace.

'Their children were crushed between them without light or air or space, so Tane, the god of nature, pushed them apart, forcing his father high into the heavens.

'Maoris say that raindrops are the tears Rangi still sheds for his lost wife, while the mists that rise from the land are Papa-Tu-Anuku's sighs.'

After a few moments of silence he swung round to look at her. Half guessing what was to come, Laura waited, her lovely face soft with sympathy, the blue of her eyes deepening to indigo, reflecting the pain she knew he was feeling.

He sighed. 'Unlike the god Tane, I was an only child but, like him, I pushed my parents apart. My father was a British subject who emigrated to New Zealand. He met my mother when he went back to England on a business trip. Though he was twenty years older than she—thirty-eight to her eighteen—they looked at each other and, to use a hackneyed phrase, it was love at first sight.

'Her parents were both dead. The only family she had was an older sister, Beatrice. So, with no one to raise any objections, they were married as soon as the arrangements could be made, and she accompanied him back to Auckland.

'For the first two or three years they were ecstatically happy. Then my mother decided she'd like to start a family. My father didn't want children, but finally she persuaded him.'

Tane paused to rub a hand across the back of his neck. 'It was a pity she did. From the day I was born I don't believe they knew a minute's happiness. They argued endlessly, always over me, and I grew up in an atmosphere of mutual bitterness and hostility, knowing that my mother, as well as my father, had come to blame and resent me.'

Once again he ran a hand over his neck as if every muscle was tense, then continued, 'When I was nearly eleven she finally left him and took me back to England. Aunt Beatrice had never married, and we lived in Northumberland with her for a while before moving south.

'When her divorce came through, my mother remarried. I was fourteen at the time. Her husband was a jealous, possessive man, and once again I became a bone of contention.

'One evening, after yet another of their furious quarrels, she turned on me and spat, "Damn you, you broke up my first marriage, now you're wrecking my second." I left home the same night.'

Laura recalled how, that first morning at Marsh House, he'd said, 'Until I met you all I knew about love was how to live without it,' and her heart bled for the unloved child he'd once been. She watched him struggle to keep his expression free from emotion, saw the firmly controlled lips, the thrust of the squared-off chin, with tenderness and compassion. More than anything she wanted to hold his dark head against her breast and comfort him.

Her voice barely audible, she whispered, 'I wish you'd told me all this before.'

'Are you saying it would have made a difference?'

'I don't know,' she confessed. 'But at least I would have *understood*.'

'Understanding doesn't magically produce a solution.'

Bleakly, she admitted, 'No, it doesn't.' And her heart felt as if it was broken. Yet she loved this man, she thought clearly. Loved his face—it never failed to move her—his athletic body, his quick brain, his honesty and integrity. She loved his gaiety and wit, his laughter and sadness, his strength, his weaknesses, the good in him, the not so good. She loved his soul, his spirit, whatever it was that made him *him*. She'd never stopped loving him. Perhaps she never would.

He gave a laugh that was more of a jeer. 'Not a very pleasant story, is it? Now you know why I didn't want a family. I knew from first-hand experience how easily a child could wreck a marriage.

'It's ironic, really, that just your *wish* for children should have had an equally devastating effect.'

Laura went to him then, and, afraid to hold him, put her hands flat against his chest, feeling his heartbeat accelerate beneath her palms. 'I'm sorry,' she breathed, adding passionately, 'I don't want you to hate me.'

Unmoving, his hands hanging by his sides, he asked, 'Why? Do you suppose that, hating you, I'm more likely to hurt you?'

'No. Love can cause far more pain than hate. I was thinking of *you*. Hate corrodes and destroys the person who feels it. There's no room for joy and happiness if you're full of hatred.'

His hands came up to cover hers, trapping them there. 'Then reverse things. Come to me, as you once did, with love. Fill me so full of joy that there's no room for hatred.'

'I can't,' she choked on a sob.

'Because you never felt any love for me?'

'No! Because I'm not a free agent now. Don't you see, it's no longer only *my* life? I have Jamie to consider.'

'So we don't even need our own child—another man's can come between us just as well,' he said bitterly.

Tearing her hands free, she cried, 'Jamie isn't coming between us any more than you came between your father and mother.' More quietly, but with utter conviction, she continued, 'It's bad enough that your childhood was miserable, but all these years you've been carrying an unnecessary burden of guilt.

'It wasn't *your* fault, shouldn't be *your* guilt. You were the victim, the scapegoat. For a marriage to break up there *has* to be something drastically, fundamentally wrong in the first place. No one can put the blame on a child.'

Suddenly inexpressibly weary, she took a faltering step forwards and rested her cheek against his shirt. His hand spread over her shining hair, and, with heart-breaking tenderness, he cradled her head against his broad chest.

After a while he raised her chin, gazing into her delicate, heart-shaped face as if he'd never seen it before, studying the straight nose, the wide mouth with its pearly teeth that weren't *quite* even, the deep blue eyes beneath winged brows, the wisps of ash-brown hair that clung to one flushed cheek like strands of silk... Then he gave a low murmur and his mouth closed over hers. He kissed her with a heady combination of hunger and need, warmth and passion.

It was the warmth, the tenderness, that melted Laura's resolve, and with it the last of the ice that had been packed around her heart for over four years.

Like someone coming home, she put her arms around his neck and held him tightly, returning his kiss, clinging to him with the same overpowering need, a hunger that was as much spiritual as bodily. Stooping, he lifted her high in his arms and, his lips still clinging closely, carried her through to the bedroom. There, laying her on the bed, he began to take off her clothes without haste.

When she was totally naked, he rolled her on to her stomach and smoothed his hand down the strong, elegant line of her spine, measuring her slim waist, following the smooth curve of her hips and buttocks and long, slender legs to her narrow feet. As if unable to get enough of the taste and feel of her, he let his lips and tongue follow his fingers, his white teeth giving her an occasional slight nip.

She squirmed and gasped, finding the stroke of his tongue in the sensitive hollow behind her knees, across the pink soles of her feet, and between each of her toes, unexpectedly, almost unbearably erotic.

When he turned her on to her back and began the same leisurely exploration, she made a husky protest. 'Tane, I can't stand much more of this.'

Having kissed her, he said gently, 'This is merely a prologue.' He planted a series of moist, nibbling baby kisses along the length of her throat and across her shoulders, before dropping to the swell of her breasts. There he suckled sweetly for a moment or two, raising her excitement to fever pitch. But, when she would have held his dark head to her, he laughed softly and moved to circle her navel with his tongue. Spreading her legs a little apart, he worked his way down the silky whiteness of one inner thigh and back up the other. Then he cupped her breasts in the palms of his hands and, while he teased the pink nipples between fingers and thumbs, his tongue flicked and probed with a delicate precision that within seconds had her taut, a spiralling response to his touch building up to a climax of feeling.

For a moment he paused, deliberately leaving her on the brink, then sent her tumbling and spinning into space, with the same heart-stopping sensations as leaving a plane at thirty thousand feet without a parachute. While she lay mindless, quivering, he stripped off his own clothes and, having lifted her so he could ease the duvet from beneath her, got into bed beside her.

Her eyes still closed, she turned towards him the way a flower turned to the sun, fitting her pliant body to the hard warmth of his, urging him over. But even when she felt his familiar weight, he still lay motionless. Surely he *wanted* her? She recalled his threat: 'I'm going to have you in my bed and keep you there until I'm sated.'

Opening her eyes, she breathed, 'Tane?'

He mimicked the thrust of possession, then asked, 'Is this really what you want? You have to be sure.' Lifting himself away, he lay beside her and, propped on one elbow, looked down into her face. 'I don't want you to wake up tomorrow morning and curse both me and yourself. If you haven't had a lover since Belmont died, sexual hunger can be a powerful force.

'That's why I insisted on a prologue. I didn't want physical needs to cloud your thinking.'

She listened to him, and, knowing how aroused he was, how tense with a desire too great for words, she marvelled at his control, his unselfishness.

'Your body is so flawless, so perfect,' he went on deeply, 'it's hard to believe you've carried a baby. I know I can't alter the fact that you've been another man's wife, borne another man's child, but every time I think about it I want to rail against fate, to smash things...'

There was such frustrated violence in his tone, such bitter regret that Laura longed to tell him the truth about her marriage. But she couldn't without admitting that Jamie was his son. And she wasn't ready to do that yet... if ever.

With a self-deprecating laugh, he muttered, 'There's ego for you... So, unable to *change* anything, all I can do is hope to make you mine once more—try to wipe out the memory of any other man. I could *take* your body, but I don't want just your body. I want *you*—your mind and your heart and your soul: *everything* that's you. And those things you have to *give*.'

He brushed her cheek with his long, lean fingers. 'Well, Laura? Do you want me to make love to you?'

If only it *was* love, as it had once been, she thought sadly. Perhaps their break-up, what he saw as her rejection, on top of his loveless childhood, had warped him so that he never would love again.

But she loved him.

Though it might not be wise, she wanted more than anything to give him this release, to generate enough light and gladness to cancel out some of the black hatred.

Her answer was clear and unequivocal. 'Yes. Yes, I do.'

CHAPTER SIX

LAURA, awakening slowly, trailing the clinging cobwebs of sleep, gradually became aware of a feeling of well-being, a mental and physical satisfaction, she hadn't known for a long time.

Stretching lazily, she discovered the slight stiffness, the tenderness, the odd ache, that a night of lovemaking left in its wake. Heart swelling, she turned towards Tane, only to realise with a sudden fierce clutch of disappointment that she was alone in the big bed.

She'd wanted to wake with him beside her, to look into his blue-grey eyes and see her own happiness and fulfilment reflected there. She'd wanted to reach out and touch him, to nestle against him and feel his arms tighten around her. She'd wanted him to smile at her, that special smile which sent her pulses racing and told her she was the only woman in the world for him.

But she was just being foolish, she scolded herself impatiently, harking back to a past which had gone, to a time when he'd loved her and she *had* been the only woman in the world for him.

Oh, yes, he still wanted her, but it was a strange, bitter kind of desire—a twisted need that owed more to rancour and jealousy than to love. Sighing, she glanced at her watch to find it was almost twelve o'clock. Pushing herself up on one elbow, she listened. The apartment was still and quiet, with an empty feel to it that made her sure Tane had gone out.

A cold cup of tea was on the bedside table, and propped against it a note which said simply, 'Thank you'. Lowering herself back on to the pillows, Laura thought about the previous night. Though she couldn't regret what had happened, in the clear light of day she knew that allowing them to become lovers again had been sheer madness. She was leaving herself wide open to yet another load of heartache.

Despite his earlier threats, Tane had known the decision had to be *hers*. He'd also been unselfish enough to try to prevent physical needs influencing that decision. So there was only herself to blame. Even at the time, she'd doubted the wisdom of it. Yet how did one measure wisdom against love?

Once upon a time, when she'd been young and naïve, she'd looked down at the world from the serenity of her own self-righteous ivory tower, and wondered how some people came to make such a mess of their lives. Now she was older, tempered by pain and loss, forced to appreciate how she'd mishandled and destroyed the most precious relationship in her life, she knew.

So where was this new, untried relationship going? Assuming he intended there to *be* any kind of relationship. What did he really want? When she'd asked him he'd answered, 'Complete control. I want you in the palm of my hand.' That, coupled with his declared intention of making her pay for leaving him, boded ill for the future... The future...

Last night she'd closed her eyes to the fact she now had to admit: they had no future. At least not together. She had Jamie to consider, and, though Tane had denied *hating* children, it didn't alter anything. In any case, he no longer loved her...

Pushing aside the weight of thoughts, she got out of bed and went into the bathroom. This was exactly as she recalled it, tiled throughout in icy pearl faintly tinged with pink, like an Arctic dawn.

She was touched to find her slip, blouse and skirt had been placed neatly over the back of a chair, and her bra and panties had been rinsed out and hung on the heated towel-rail. Beneath his all-male arrogance, his toughness and strength, his cool, sometimes cynical veneer, Tane was sensitive and considerate. A kind, thoughtful man, who, if he hadn't been warped by such parents, would have made a good father.

Sighing, Laura stepped beneath the shower.

Fifteen minutes later, refreshed and feeling more cheerful, she went into the living-room. Her handbag was lying on the coffee-table, where she'd placed it the previous evening. Shock stopped her breath. On top of it lay her wedding-ring.

Why had Tane returned it? Had he given it back to signify he'd got what he wanted and she was free to go? Was that why he'd left the penthouse empty? Had the 'Thank you' been derisory, a crow of triumph?

Though she'd told herself they had no future together, beneath the ice of common sense had lurked a forlorn hope that the road ahead might become clear. Now she felt dazed and despairing, like a fugitive who had turned into a cul-de-sac. There was no way forward, and she was unable to go back.

How long she stood there motionless, Laura never knew. Eventually she pulled herself together, and dropped the ring into her bag. Throwing on her coat, she made her way down to the luxurious foyer and out into the street, refusing the commissionaire's offer of a taxi with a shake of her head.

For a while she walked blindly, with no clear idea of where she wanted to go, or what she intended to do. Yesterday's chill wind had blown itself away, and the day was cool and cloudy and so still that the very air seemed to hold its breath.

Just ahead was a bus-stop with a few people waiting. As Laura drew level with the queue, a bus juddered to a halt. Catching sight of the familiar number, she followed the last person on, her decision made for her.

It was was only a short walk at the other end. Molly answered the door promptly, and, showing no surprise, said, 'So there you are. Come and have a nice cup of tea.'

A small shape hurtled from the kitchen and grabbed Laura around the knees. 'Mummy! Mummy!'

She stooped to hug the sturdy little body to her, her heart full to overflowing, as it always was when she saw him. 'Hello, darling...I'm sorry I didn't see you yesterday.'

'I did go to a party,' he said importantly. 'It was Mark's birfday.'

'Did you have a good time?'

'We had jelly an' cake an' ice-cweam, an' Becky was sick.'

'Becky is Mark's little sister,' Molly explained.

'He's going to have anover one,' Jamie chimed in. 'Only he wants a bruvver this time. When do I get a bruvver?'

'Well, I...' Laura glanced up and gaped stupidly.

Leaning negligently against the jamb of the kitchen door was Tane.

Following her gaze, Jamie announced, '*He's* going to help me move the sand-pit and put up the swing you bought me.' Hopping excitedly from foot to foot, he demanded, 'When can we start?'

'As soon as you're ready,' Molly said briskly. 'Go and put on your anorak and wellies...and don't look like that!'

'Like what?'

'As if you've just swallowed a worm.'

He giggled, then wheedled, 'I don't *have* to wear my wellies, do I?'

'It rained hard last night, so the ground will still be wet.'

'I don't mind if my feets is wet.'

'Well, *I* do. Move!'

Looking resigned, Jamie allowed himself to be chivvied into the playroom.

'Hello, Laura,' Tane said softly. Then, smiling at her stupefication, 'Lost your tongue?'

'What are you doing here?' she croaked.

'Waiting to help construct a new play area,' he answered innocently.

'I mean, why——?' At that instant Jamie came bouncing back, wearing a green and yellow anorak and red shiny wellingtons, bright as jujubes.

He was a robust child, tall for his age, with an unruly mop of dark curly hair and his mother's cornflower-blue eyes. His other features were Tane's and, with an insight born of knowledge, Laura could tell he was going to grow up to be very like his father.

The thought held as much pain as pleasure.

Her emotions were complicated, twisted, like a skein of multi-coloured silks. She'd never thought to see them together, and it made her feel stricken, breathless, as if her heart were being squeezed tightly in a giant fist.

Beaming at Tane, Jamie assured him, 'I'm weady.'

'Do you want any help?' Laura asked.

'Do we need a woman in the working party?' Tane enquired lazily.

'No,' Jamie decided. Then, craftily, 'If the van comes past will *you* buy me an ice-cweam?'

'Is that allowed?' Tane sought permission from Molly.

'Only on the understanding he eats all his tea.'

'Well?' Tane cocked an eyebrow at the child.

His promise given with far too much alacrity to inspire confidence, Jamie thrust a grubby paw into Tane's hand, and began to lead him out the back way.

'Everything's in the shed,' Molly called after him, 'and the key's on——'

'I know where it is!' Jamie bristled with indignation. 'I'll show him.' A few seconds later the door closed behind them.

Like someone in a dream, Laura went to the window to watch them walk down the garden hand in hand and, judging by Tane's bent head, deep in amicable conversation as they disappeared into the shed.

The questions came thick and fast. What was Tane up to? Why was he being so nice to Jamie? Had his attitude towards children changed? Or was he just playing a part?

Having no answers, Laura sighed, feeling confused and insecure. It had taken her a long time to build a new life. In only a few days Tane had succeeded in turning that life upside-down. She'd stopped wearing her wedding-ring, she'd admitted to herself that she still loved him, and, with no real understanding of what *his* feelings were—could someone who *hated* be so tender?—she'd been to bed with him. Now here she was without the least idea of where she stood, or where she was going...

'Come and have that cup of tea,' Molly suggested, clearly convinced that a cup of tea was the panacea for all of life's ills. 'You look as if you could do with it.' Laura followed the older woman into the kitchen and sat down at the pine table. Busying herself with the kettle and teapot, Molly remarked, 'From the look of amazement on your face, I take it you didn't know he was going to be here?'

Laura shook her head. 'When did he come?'

'He arrived just before lunch and, cool as you like, said he'd take me to pick Jamie up. In view of your phone call yesterday I wasn't at all sure you'd want him to see the bairn, so I tried to say "No, thank you". But I soon realised I was on a hiding to nothing. He's a formidable man, so he is. He wouldn't be put off, and I couldn't not go.' Molly sounded anxious.

'No, no, of course you couldn't.'

'I must say he caused quite a sensation at the playschool. Miss Graves went all pink and flustered and dropped a pile of painting books, and Mrs Donald positively goggled at him. I've known men in my time who sparked with charm enough to kindle dry grass, but Himself could set fire to a swamp, so he could!

'Anyway, when we got back home I asked him, in a voice that could have blistered paint, if he was intending to stay for lunch. He gave me a smile that would have made any woman his slave for life, and said "yes please".

'So I told him we were having baked beans on toast. Even that didn't wipe the smile off his face. He vowed they were his favourite. But I'd seen him shudder. So then I asked him, Was his appetite good? Would I be needing to open more than one tin?

'He's a man with a rare sense of humour. His eyes were dancing, but he answered gravely that he thought one tin would be *quite* sufficient.'

Aware that Tane *hated* baked beans, Laura felt sure it would.

'I gave him a good big dollop,' Molly added with cheerful malice.

Her own sense of humour surfacing briefly, Laura chuckled. 'And did he back down?'

'Not he. But the bairn and he made a deal. Jamie ate most of the beans, and Himself had the soggy toast. He remarked it was a pity you weren't there to enjoy the treat, so I asked him where you were. He said he'd left you in bed. You were having a sleep in, but you'd almost certainly be along later.'

Feeling her cheeks grow hot, Laura said uncomfortably, 'I...I ought to explain about——'

'You don't need to explain,' Molly said, when Laura hesitated. 'You don't need to tell me anything you don't want to tell me. It isn't my business.' But all the same she was agog, her greeny opal eyes sparkling with excitement and curiosity.

Feeling she owed the other woman an explanation, Laura braced herself and said as phlegmatically as possible, 'Tane and I were once engaged. Our wedding was only a week or so away when we...I realised it was a mistake...'

'A mistake, was it? Did you feel a man as gorgeous as Himself wouldn't be faithful?'

'No, no, it wasn't that. We were just...incompatible.'

'You seem compatible enough to me, but then, there's more to marriage than four bare legs in a bed. And I don't know him that well; he may be a swine to live with.'

About to refute that suggestion, Laura changed her mind and let it go.

'So you parted...?' Molly prodded.

Laura swallowed, just the memory of it bringing a lump to her throat. 'Yes. At first I didn't know where to go. You see, I'd given up my flat. Then I thought of David. We'd been friends since we were at the orphanage together, so I went to him. A few weeks later I——'

'Found you were expecting Tane's baby?' Molly supplied.

'Yes. How...?'

'Sure and haven't I got eyes in me head? Then there's the name. I always thought Jamie's middle name was an unusual one.' All attempt at self-restraint forgotten, Molly asked eagerly, 'So then what happened?'

'When David found out he asked me to marry him.'

'No, I mean what happened with Himself?'

'Nothing. He...he never knew. Until he turned up a few days ago I hadn't seen him for over four years. He thinks Jamie is David's child.'

'Does he, now?' Molly asked thoughtfully. 'So that's why you didn't want him to see the bairn? And why he was so keen to do just that...' Becoming aware of how disturbed Laura looked, Molly added, 'Ah, well, he may not notice the resemblance. Men can be very blind, and it's always a great deal harder to see a likeness to oneself.'

Tugging at the chain around her neck, Laura went on, 'That's why I had to lie about Jamie's birthday, say he was three months younger than he is.'

'I wondered about that at the time. But *did* you have to? Thinking logically, you're a widow with a child to support. His child. He doesn't look to me as if he's short of money. Perhaps if you told him the truth...'

'No, no, I can't do that. He doesn't like children.'

'Stuff and nonsense!' Molly said rudely. 'Those two were getting on like a house on fire. Took to each other straight away, so they did. In any case, you can't let a man escape all responsibility for his actions by saying he doesn't like the result.'

'I don't want him to know!' Laura sounded almost panic-stricken. 'There's more to it than that, other reasons for not telling him.'

When it became clear Laura wasn't going to elaborate on those reasons, Molly went off at a tangent. 'I see you're not wearing your wedding-ring?'

'No, I . . . Tane didn't want me to . . .'

'Jealous, eh?' Molly summed up shrewdly. 'If he's jealous and taking such an interest in Jamie, he maybe has *plans* . . .'

Knowing Tane, he almost certainly *had*, Laura thought, though probably not the kind Molly meant. She shivered suddenly, and it wasn't with cold.

By the time the sand-pit had been re-sited, and the swing put up and duly tested, it was getting on for four-thirty. Laura had been hovering by the window for a good hour, watching the man and boy. Now, feeling the same mingling of pleasure and pain, she saw the pair walk up the path together, still talking, still apparently well satisfied with each other's company.

Jamie burst in, his energy in no way depleted, and announced, 'Next time he comes he's going to take me to the park and on the—on the . . .'

'Boating lake,' Tane supplied. He met Laura's eyes and gave her a disarming smile. 'With your permission, of course.'

'Well, if Mr Carlson does come again——' Laura began.

'He's coming gen,' Jamie insisted. 'He pwomised.'

'And I always keep my promises,' Tane added smoothly.

To Laura, the assurance sounded almost like a threat.

Having followed this little exchange with interest, Molly asked, 'Will you be staying for tea now?'

'Thank you, but I think not,' Tane refused easily. 'We ought to be getting off.'

Not sure whether to be pleased or sorry, Laura made no demur, and they all walked down the path together. At the gate she thanked Molly, then stooped to hug Jamie. 'Bye, darling, be a good boy.' She hated leaving him and, as always, her voice was husky. 'I'll come again soon.'

'When, Mummy?'

She glanced up at Tane, her face unguarded, vulnerable, before answering, 'I'm not sure, darling. But *soon*, I promise.'

'And Mummy always keeps her promises,' Tane said. As he helped her into the car, he added *sotto voce*, 'Except when it's a promise to marry.'

Laura gave him a look of reproach, but when their eyes met, as with Lancelot and Guinevere, it was hers that fell. Twisting in her seat, she smiled and waved until the two figures standing at the gate were out of sight.

As they made their way down a quiet stretch of road, Tane reached over and picked up her left hand, his thumb rubbing over the pale mark left by her wedding-ring. 'Why didn't you put it back, Laura?'

'I—I don't know. I just felt as if I *couldn't*, after what had happened.' He said nothing further, but she was oddly convinced it was the answer he'd wanted.

For a while he drove in silence, then, slanting her a glance, remarked, 'I thought you said Jamie was like his father?'

'In a lot of ways he is,' she answered levelly.

'You told me Belmont was fair.'

'Yes, he was. Jamie has my colouring.'

'He has your *eyes*,' Tane corrected. Adding, after a moment, 'Molly was right in saying he was very forward for his age. Anyone would take him for nearer four.'

Laura sat still as a statue. After a moment or two, when Tane said nothing further, she gradually released the breath she was holding, and tried to relax. But it proved to be impossible. Curbing the impulse to pour out all the questions seething in her brain, she queried only, 'Why did you go to Molly's?'

She thought from his demeanour that he wasn't going to reply, then he answered abruptly, 'I wanted to see Jamie.'

It was taking a risk but she had to ask. 'Why?'

'I don't *know* why,' he said in a tortured voice. 'All I know is I felt a fierce-driven need to see this child another man had fathered.'

It seemed that, in saying Tane was jealous, Molly had summed up the situation correctly. But he hadn't wanted children himself, so it didn't appear to make sense. There was a long silence before Laura ventured, 'Where are we going?'

'Home,' he returned laconically. 'And then out for a meal.'

'I need some clothes,' she protested.

'Yes, I've been thinking about that,' he said. 'But can't you manage for tonight?'

'I'd like something fresh to put on, and a nightdress.'

'A nightdress?' He gave her a quizzical glance. 'Whatever for?'

Feeling her cheeks grow warm, she steadfastly ignored both his words and look. If she allowed herself to be disturbed by his teasing she could spend half her time in heated confusion.

At the crossroads he changed direction, and soon they were drawing up outside the Lulworth building. Taking the key from her hand, he opened the door and accompanied her through the gloom of the shop. The air was cool, and a faint mustiness mingled with the smell of books and old leather, paper and printer's ink.

With being closed up, the dingy back room smelt stale, and Tane made a grimace of distaste. Laura felt bitterly ashamed, mortified, and, the day's tension snapping like an over-stretched rubber band, she turned on him, a martial light in her eyes. 'This is my home. All I have. If it upsets you so much, why don't you just go? Get back to your smart penthouse and leave me in peace to live my own life!'

Unmoved by both her anger and the sudden glint of tears, Tane leaned against the door-frame, tall and powerfully attractive, and regarded her coolly.

'I ought to have the shop open——' Laura's voice cracked with despair. 'There's a quarter's rent due, I owe Molly for taking care of Jamie, I owe——'

'You owe *me*.' Tane's expression was hard, unrelenting. 'Pack what you need, and let's get out of here.'

She felt an urge to rebel, to dig in her heels and refuse to budge. He couldn't *force* her to go with him. But she was afraid of his ruthlessness, his implacability, and this fear robbed her of strength and will-power, and weakened her fighting spirit. Or was it simply that her own mind played the traitor, and, though she knew what absolute folly it was, subconsciously she *wanted* to go with him?

For a few seconds she stood irresolute, then, taking refuge behind a veneer of calm, pulled an overnight case from the cupboard and began to push in undies, some clothes and a change of shoes.

In the meantime, Tane prowled around restlessly, peering into the cupboard and opening drawers. As soon as she closed the lid of the case, he snapped the locks shut, and carried it out to his car.

As they were caught in the evening rush, it was nearly six-thirty by the time they reached the penthouse. There, Tane broke the silence to ask, 'Did you have any lunch?' Laura shook her head. His voice neutral, neither friendly nor unfriendly, he remarked, 'Then you must be more than ready to eat.'

She didn't feel hungry so much as tired and unkempt. 'I'd like to shower and change before we go out.'

'Of course,' he agreed politely.

While he watched her she opened the case and unpacked her night things, some underwear, and a flowered dress—all pretty but cheap. Aware that he was studying them without favour, she lifted her chin ready to do battle, but he said nothing.

With the beginnings of a headache, she went into the bathroom and, instead of showering, ran a bath. Climbing in, she washed herself, then stretched full length in the warm, scented water, and let her eyelids close.

She opened her eyes, bewildered and disorientated, to find the water distinctly cool, and Tane standing looking down at her. As she struggled to her feet and stepped out on to the tufted mat, he took a towelling bath-robe from behind the door, and handed it to her. She pulled it on and tied the belt.

His short white robe was calf-length on her and the sleeves hung down over her hands before she rolled them up. Without shoes she scarcely came up to his shoulder.

He took in her shiny nose, the tendrils of steam-dampened hair, her bare feet and wet legs. A gleam in his eye, he remarked with satisfaction, 'That's how I like you to look.' With a hand beneath her chin, he lifted her face to his merciless scrutiny, leaving her no place to hide. 'Mind and body, I want you helpless, defenceless, open to me.' His voice was a husky whisper. 'The mere thought of it acts like an aphrodisiac.'

Shudders began to run through her. He felt them and smiled. One of his hands slipped inside the robe to cup the damp warmth of her breast, while his tongue searched for and found the hollow at the base of her throat. She gave a stifled gasp as his mouth closed over the sensitive skin, sucking and nibbling erotically in a tingling love-bite.

Her heart was banging against her ribs with sickening force before he lifted his head and put her away from him. 'We'd better go and eat. When I start making love to you I want the whole night ahead of me.'

Laura's throat went dry and her stomach clenched as his words sent her on a sexual roller-coaster ride. Holding on to as much composure as possible, she finished drying herself and got dressed, while Tane showered and shaved.

His presence disturbed and distracted her, but after last night she could hardly ask to have the bathroom to herself, she thought wryly. But, very aware of his naked bronzed body as he padded about, she made a point of not looking at him while she hurriedly applied a dab of make-up and pulled a comb through her hair.

As she reached the safety of the door he spoke her name. She looked round and blushed vividly.

He grinned and said, 'You see how just your presence affects me, even when you're keeping your eyes averted like some little novice from a nunnery?'

She fled, his soft laughter following her.

When he strolled into the living-room some five minutes later he looked handsome and virile and, considering he'd had as little sleep as she the previous night, and expended considerably more energy, remarkably fresh.

Just the thought brought embarrassed colour into Laura's cheeks.

Noting her agitation, he remarked, 'It's hard to believe you've ever been a married woman. You seem as pure and innocent, as *modest* as you did when we first met.'

'Hardly,' she managed drily.

They took a taxi to Capone's, a well-known restaurant just off Piccadilly, with a 'twenties' décor and superb food.

Though Tane kept the conversation light and general, Laura was unable to relax. She could feel his magnetism surrounding her like an invisible force-field, and those handsome blue-grey eyes had a disconcerting habit of conveying messages and promises that had nothing to do with what he was actually saying.

But when he began to tell her about an unusual business deal he'd been involved in, interested, she asked a number of pertinent questions, and soon they were talking with something approaching the ease they'd once enjoyed. At the conclusion of his tale, she commented, 'If you hadn't stepped in, Daneton might have been ruined.'

Tane's shoulders lifted in a slight shrug. 'He was comparatively new in the business world, still wet behind the ears, with neither the experience nor the capital needed to carry off such a scheme.'

On an impulse, she asked, 'How did *you* get a start in business? What happened after you left your mother and stepfather?'

There was a pause, as if he needed to steel himself to talk about his younger days, then he said, 'They washed their hands of me, and, rather than go into a home, I went to live with Aunt Beatrice. It must have been very inconvenient to have had a surly fourteen-year-old thrust on her, but if it was she never showed it.

'She was kind in a dry, unemotional way, and did her best for me, making sure I stayed at school until I was eighteen, and helping me financially when I went on to university.

'I was in my final year at Durham when my mother and stepfather were killed in a motorway pile-up, and then, just before I graduated, my father died of a heart-attack.

'He left everything he owned to me, but Aunt Beatrice didn't fancy living in New Zealand, and I didn't want to leave her, so I decided to start my own business here.

'In the beginning I had my share of failures, but I learned from them, and on the whole I was lucky. Inside five years I'd quadrupled what my father left me. By the time I was thirty, to all intents and purposes I was happy and successful, at the top of the ladder, and wealthy.' His voice, his expression, were full of wry self-mockery.

'So long as you got there ethically, there's nothing wrong with being at the top of the ladder and wealthy,' she protested.

'It has some compensations,' he agreed, with a note in his voice that made her vaguely uneasy.

By the time their coffee was served, Laura had begun to droop wearily. 'Tired?' Tane asked, and, knowing the answer, summoned the waiter with just a glance. Within fifteen minutes the bill was paid and their taxi had dropped them at Hunwick Court.

With an arm around her shoulders, he led her across the thickly carpeted foyer and into the lift.

Inside the penthouse he stepped behind her to slip the coat from her shoulders. She shivered as he moved the gleaming ash-brown hair and touched his lips to the warmth of her nape.

When he tossed her coat aside and turned her into his arms, though she knew she shouldn't allow herself to be drawn any deeper into this abortive relationship, she lifted her face as if there was no help for it, and he kissed her the way a man dying of thirst drank at a spring of cool, sweet water.

In bed he made love to her with a dizzying combination of passion and tenderness, then, nestling her close, he settled her head on his shoulder and said, 'Sleep now.'

Laura awoke to find it was morning and once again she was alone in the big bed. But this time she could hear sounds of movement—the cheerful chink of crockery. Pulling on a thin cotton dressing-gown, she padded through to the attractive, modern kitchen. True to the vagaries of the British climate, the day was clear and bright, and the french windows were open, with breakfast set on the sunny terrace.

Having finished pouring freshly squeezed orange juice into two glasses, Tane dropped a kiss on the tip of her nose and, as she took a seat at the table, sat down opposite. He looked coolly elegant in lightweight grey trousers with a striped silk shirt and matching tie.

Laura helped herself to a piece of crisp toast and, noticing his jacket was draped over a chair-back, was just about to ask if he was going into the office, when he said casually, 'Don't be too long over breakfast—we're booked on a morning flight to Paris.'

CHAPTER SEVEN

'PARIS?' There was consternation in Laura's tone and in her blue eyes.

The half-smile died from Tane's lips. 'I thought you might like the idea.'

In the old days, when she was young and free, she would have been deliriously happy at the thought of going to Paris with Tane. But she was no longer young or free. She was a woman with a business to run, commitments. Even so, part of her still wanted to eagerly accept, to say, 'I *do* like the idea.' Curbing the traitorous impulse, she asked coldly, 'When did you decide on this?'

'Yesterday.'

'You should have discussed it with me first. I *don't* like the idea. I don't want to leave Jamie.'

'When you're at the shop you don't see him during the week,' Tane pointed out flatly. 'So what difference does it make? And you can phone every day... twice a day if it'll make you happy.'

'I don't want to go,' she said stubbornly.

His dark brows drew together in a frown. 'Most women jump at the chance of a trip to Paris.'

Most women. His ex-mistresses.

Laura sat bolt upright. 'I don't want to go to Paris,' she repeated. 'I want to open my shop. I need the money.'

'As we agreed last night, being wealthy has its compensations. You don't have to worry about money.'

'But I *do*. I'm on my own with a child to support. I *work* for a living. I've no intention of becoming dependent on you.'

'That isn't how I see it.' He was obviously keeping his temper in check only with an effort.

'It's how *I* see it,' she retorted. 'That's why I refuse to go to Paris with you.'

Flatly, he said, 'But you haven't any choice in the matter.'

'Of course I have a choice. You can't *make* me go.'

He poured coffee for them both before asking, 'What kind of lease do you have on the shop?'

Laura's face whitened. It was a short-term lease due for renewal next month, as well he knew.

Stirring a spoonful of demerara sugar into his coffee, he went on conversationally, 'Once the formalities are completed and the money changes hands, the Lulworth building is mine. I could leave it as it is for a year or so; on the other hand I may want to start refurbishing it straight away. If I choose the latter, the present tenants may need to move out and either surrender or renegotiate their leases.'

Eyes narrowed to gleaming slits against the sun, he suggested, 'A few days in Paris would give us both time to decide on the best course of action.'

She unclenched her teeth to say sweetly, 'I'm afraid I don't know where my passport is.'

Tane felt in the inside pocket of his jacket and produced it.

'Where did you get that?' she demanded.

'From the top drawer of your chest.'

'You're a devil!' she said angrily.

'I'm what you've made me.'

                    *   *   *

Hotel Lancier was in Rue Lepic—a quiet backwater flanked by imposing buildings of light greyish stone. Its broad, flagged pavements and cobble-stoned square were shaded by dusty lime trees.

Their suite, a large bedroom with a sumptuous bathroom and a mirrored and draped sitting-room, was situated at the rear, overlooking a secluded courtyard. A weedy, narrow-shouldered bell-boy carried up their cases, and departed clutching a generous tip.

Resentful, feeling the need to fight back, Laura had embarked on a programme of passive resistance. Her case held only the barest of bare necessities—Tane had watched her pack it with a gleam in his eyes which ought to have made her wary—and during the journey she'd answered only in monosyllables when spoken to, and made no attempt at conversation.

Polite and apparently unperturbed, he had passed no comment on her unsociability, but she was well aware that her attitude had angered him. Now he glanced at her and asked, 'Do I take it this is your first trip to Paris?'

Without looking at him, she replied, 'Yes.'

'Would you like to go out and see something of the city?'

'If you want me to.'

'From the lack of enthusiasm, anyone not hearing the question could be forgiven for thinking you'd been asked to sign your own death-warrant.' When she stayed mute he eyed the creased dress she'd travelled in, and asked, 'I presume you haven't anything better to wear?'

'No.'

'Then it's time you had.' His voice was smooth and polished, with the cutting edge of a diamond. 'But first would you like to put this on?' He produced her engagement-ring.

She shook her head, putting her hands behind her back like a recalcitrant schoolgirl.

'It would make a difference to your status,' he pointed out slowly.

'I don't want to wear it.'

'Very well.' He replaced the box in his pocket. 'I thought we'd have lunch on the Butte Montmartre.'

Some half an hour later, a taxi dropped them at the bottom of Rue André-del-Sarte and, Tane leading the way, they climbed the dusty steps and turned left on to Rue Bernard-Palissy. The cobbled street, sunny and picturesque, was full of the unique odours of France: espresso coffee and Pernod, perfume and drains, garlic and Gauloises, mingled with the smell of freshly baked bread and croissants from the neighbourhood patisserie.

Though it was the beginning of August, the holiday month when most Parisians took their children and poured out of the city for *les grandes vacances*, the pavement cafés were crowded, local artists and red-faced tourists jostling elbow to elbow.

A table beneath a broad-striped umbrella became vacant, and Tane steered her towards it. In spite of her determination to dampen any reaction, Laura found herself absorbed by the colourful scene. She watched as a waiter, his circular tray held aloft on one hand, glided between the packed tables like a dancer...

'What would you like to eat?' Tane asked.

Her face carefully blank, and avoiding his eyes, she answered with studied indifference, 'I couldn't care less.' And then felt a momentary panic in case he retaliated by ordering snails or frogs' legs. But, even if he did, she didn't *have* to eat them, she reminded herself.

He ordered *omelettes aux fines herbes* and a bottle of Chablis. His French was easy and fluent, his accent good, and she wondered how many trips he'd made with his various mistresses.

It was hot and sunny, with a cloudless, Mediterranean-blue sky, and, had the circumstances been other than they were, Laura would have thoroughly enjoyed herself. As it was, head bent, she concentrated on appearing indifferent.

After a couple of unsuccessful attempts to draw her into conversation, Tane relapsed into silence. Though his face was expressionless, she knew he was seething with anger. As soon as the meal was over, he paid the bill and escorted her to a taxi he'd signalled when it had stopped to drop off a couple of American tourists.

'I thought we'd go shopping,' he informed her, his tone determinedly polite. 'Unless there's anything you'd rather do?'

Looking into the middle-distance, Laura moved her shoulders in a slight shrug. 'I really don't mind.'

Tightly, he said, 'I'm getting fed up with this passive resistance, and more than a little tired of your looking past me and through me but never *at* me. I've made up my mind that before the day's out we'll have an end to it.'

Laura didn't answer but, afraid of his ruthlessness, of the cold intelligence which fuelled it, a chill ran through her.

He'd said *shopping*, and she was surprised when the taxi drew up outside what appeared to be a stylish private house. They crossed the tree-shaded pavement to a door with a black ornamental grille, and Tane rang the bell before escorting her inside.

A chic, silver-haired woman met and greeted him with a mixture of enthusiasm and respect, then led the way across an echoing marble foyer. After one swift, assessing glance at Laura's off-the-peg dress, she averted her eyes and ignored the girl completely.

Tane was talking fast, much too fast for Laura's schoolgirl French to follow, and using his long, well-shaped hands expressively. Every so often Madame would answer, *'Oui, monsieur, certainement,'* or, *'Oui, monsieur, je comprends parfaitement.'*

As they entered a large, ornate salon with marble walls and sparkling chandeliers, she snapped her fingers. A *vendeuse* and several helpers came scurrying.

While Madame gave swift orders, two small gilt-backed chairs were produced and set side by side at the edge of what appeared to be several acres of crimson carpet. When Laura hesitated, Tane's hand on her upper arm exerted enough downward pressure to make it expedient for her to sit. He took a seat by her side and put a proprietorial arm around her shoulders.

The *vendeuse*, a sharp-featured woman with black hair cut very short and pearl studs in her rather large lobes, asked, 'What size does *madame* take?'

Subduing an impulse to say, 'I'm *here*, why don't you ask me?' Laura clenched her teeth.

Having answered, Tane used his free hand to turn Laura's face to his, while he queried silkily, 'That's right, isn't it, *ma chérie*?' She gave him a look of intense dislike and said nothing. If he thought she was going to allow him to buy her clothes he had another think coming!

It wasn't long before she learnt she had no say in the matter. She also learnt the full meaning of the word humiliation.

When she would have risen and left, Tane's arm, heavy across her shoulders, kept her there. Unable to find sufficient courage to create a scene, she sat like a statue while a whole wardrobe of fabulous clothes was modelled for them, starting with coats and skirts, dresses and suits, and going on to evening wear and accessories.

From time to time Tane would nod, a brief discussion with the *vendeuse* would ensue, and any desired colour or detail change would be noted, before that model disappeared through the red velvet curtains at the far end of the salon, and the next one took her place.

None of the women so much as glanced at Laura, and she realised now what Tane had meant when he said that wearing the engagement-ring would make a difference to her status. Instead of being regarded as a rich man's plaything, of no account in her own right, she would have been accorded the respect due to his future wife.

Last, but not least, a selection of beautiful nightwear and underwear was displayed.

Clearly enjoying himself, Tane chose liberally. Then, having signified his approval of a daring black lace teddy, he added coolly, 'But the bust section would need to be a size larger. *Madame* is quite deceptive.'

Mortified colour burnt in Laura's cheeks, but somehow she kept her head high until the business was completed and they were outside on the shady boulevard. As soon as the door closed behind them, she turned on him, and spat, 'If you think for one minute that I'm going to——'

Ready for the explosion he'd known was imminent, Tane neatly hooked her feet from beneath her, before pulling her against him. Off balance, she was unable to struggle as his mouth covered hers, stopping the furious tirade.

After a few seconds he lifted his head to say quietly, 'If you want a fight I'll indulge you later, but I refuse to quarrel in the street. If you try it I'll have to take the appropriate action. Paris is a city of lovers—no one will mind, and I'll enjoy it, so it's up to you.' Seeing her lips were clamped tight, he set her on her feet again, restoring her balance, and suggested, 'Perhaps we should walk for a while and dissipate some of that adrenalin.'

They walked for more than two hours. Gradually Laura simmered down and began to look about her, charmed by this most beautiful of cities.

It was high summer. Paris was sweltering in temperatures exceeding thirty degrees, and in the Tuileries people clustered round the fountains and sought the shade of the trees. Apart from pointing out various sights and places of interest, Tane had said nothing since suggesting they should walk. Now, as they approached the Louvre, he remarked, 'You're looking tired. I think, if you're agreeable, we might have dinner then take a taxi back.'

Laura, who up until then hadn't spoken a single word, said distantly, 'Very well.'

He took her to La Ronde, a luxurious circular restaurant with a striking green and gold décor. Without surprise, she noticed heads turn discreetly to watch them pass. Tane had an aura of power, a natural authority, which, combined with his good looks and striking physique, drew all eyes. Observing how the other women present were dressed, she found herself wishing she was wearing something smarter, more in keeping, until it occurred to her that that was why he'd taken her to that fashionable place.

The realisation fanned her smouldering anger, bringing it to red-hot life. Watching her face, he smiled sardonically, and advised, 'Don't let it spoil your appetite—the lamb Navarre here is superb.'

By the time the splendid meal was finished and they'd partaken of coffee and fine old brandy, Tane's quietly spoken request had been met, and a taxi awaited them at the door.

When they arrived at the hotel, he collected the big, old-fashioned key and they took the lift straight up to their second-floor suite. Having unlocked the door, he led the way into the sitting-room, then turned to face her, his grey-blue eyes holding an unmistakable challenge. 'Well, Laura?'

Beneath a thin veneer of calm, her emotions were still in a turmoil. She dipped her head and looked down at her clenched hands.

'What excellent control,' he mocked. 'But I'd just as soon you released some of that pent-up fury by flying at me.'

At first anger had blinded her to every other consideration and she'd wanted to do just that. She'd felt a fierce primitive urge to hit out at him, to rake her nails down his handsome face and draw blood. Now, though still raw, flayed by the deliberate humiliation he'd inflicted on her, she had regained her self-control, and along with it some degree of self-respect, and was shocked by the violence of her earlier feelings.

In a familiar questioning gesture, he raised a dark brow. 'No?' Sounding disappointed, he added, 'So it's going to be a battle of words?'

Common sense told Laura it was no use trying to take him on verbally. He was clever and ruthless, his brain swift and deadly, his intelligence so much greater than hers that he would be able to run rings around her effortlessly.

When she remained dumb, he said, 'What I won't allow you to do is sulk. I want things out in the open. I want to know what you're thinking, feeling.'

Quietly, but her blue eyes flashing, she said, 'All right, I'll tell you. I think you're an absolute swine. I feel as demeaned and mortified as you *intended* me to feel. You deliberately treated me as if I were your...' her voice shook '...your kept woman.'

'You are.'

'I am *not*! I didn't want to come to Paris. I've never willingly taken anything from you.'

He shrugged lazily. 'Very well, we'll change the description to mistress. What's the difference?'

'There's a great deal of difference. A kept woman is just that: someone who is *kept* in exchange for her favours. A mistress is usually an independent woman who chooses a lover on equal terms. But I am *not* your mistress either.'

'Have you forgotten that of your own volition you've spent the last two nights in my bed?'

'I haven't forgotten anything.' She lifted her chin. 'Spending two nights in your bed makes me a fool, but it doesn't make me your mistress. For me to count as your mistress our relationship would have to be a *continuing* one, and I've no intention of allowing it to continue.'

His jaw tightened and he gave her a look that sizzled along her nerve-ends. 'We'll see, shall we? When you're lying in my arms tonight——'

'I won't be in your arms tonight. I won't go to bed with you.'

'Oh, I think you will.' Reading her thoughts, he added derisively, 'And of your own free will. You're a passionate woman with the same fierce needs that I have.

I sometimes think you must have scared that poor sickly husband of yours. You were probably more than he knew how to handle.'

Laura's anger erupted like molten larva spewing from a volcano. 'Leave David out of this,' she cried furiously. 'You're not fit to mention his name.'

Turning, she headed blindly for the door, but Tane was there before her, leaning with his back against the panels. With a recklessness born of desperation, she stormed, 'Get out of my way! I'm leaving.'

'I think not.'

'You can't stop me; I'm a free woman.'

Shaking his head, he said, 'But you're not free. You're mine, and you know it.'

He moved towards her and the next second she was flat on her back on the big couch with him beside her. She tried to struggle up, but he held her down with the utmost ease.

'If you don't let me go I'll scream.' She drew a deep breath, preparatory to putting her threat into action. His grip slackened, allowing her for one brief moment to believe she'd won, then his mouth swooped to cover hers.

She tried to fight him but, with his hands clamped on her upper arms, he kissed her mercilessly. The kiss went on and on until, with no breath left, and her senses reeling, she went limp. Only then did his lips become gentle, persuasive, incredibly sweet, moving over her face, touching her eyelids, investigating her delicate ears and throat. Running his fingers through the length of her hair, he spread it over the cushion, burying his face in the silken strands.

Clinging to the coat-tails of sanity, Laura tried to ignore it when those tantalising lips returned to brush her temples, her neat nose, the clean line of her jaw.

But, when they touched the corner of her mouth and lingered there, helplessly caught up, tossed in a sea of wanting, she turned her head towards the source of the pleasure, blindly seeking his mouth.

It closed over hers, the thrust of his tongue sending excitement sky-rocketing, while his hands began to remove her clothes and stroke over her body, bringing it to singing life. Her eyes shut tight, her mind engulfed, she lost all sense of time or place. Drunk with desire, she forgot the stand she was trying to make, forgot her pride, her self-respect, her fear of the future, even her attempt at self-preservation. There was nothing except this man, and what he was making her feel and experience.

Then she became dimly aware of being alone and bereft, but the mists that had obliterated her mind were clearing away only slowly. Incapable as yet of coherent thought, she pushed herself up into a sitting position.

Taking her hands, he pulled her to her feet, and, facing one of the long mirrors, held her in front of him. She saw two people, both bare to the waist. A man, bronzed and muscular, dark and handsome as Gabriel himself, and a golden-skinned, full-breasted woman, hectically flushed, the mouth red and moist, the blue eyes glazed with passion.

'Look...look at yourself. See what I mean?' His tone held triumph. 'Your pride balks at the terms "kept woman" or "mistress", but that doesn't alter the fact that you're *mine*.

'That first night, before I made love to you, I gave you time to think, the chance to back out, but you didn't take it.' He bent his head and touched his lips to the side of her neck, while his hands came up to cup her breasts.

'Now it's too late. You're mine for as long as I choose to keep you.'

'No...' Laura tried to deny his words and her own feelings, but, trapped by a steel net woven from circumstances and the strength of her love for him, her resistance was at an end, and they both knew it.

It was next morning before, thinking over the events of the previous evening, Laura realised that Tane had deliberately trailed his coat for her to pounce on. He'd *wanted* her to lose her temper, *wanted* her anger out in the open. That was why he'd spoken slightingly of David. He was a clever, devious opponent, she conceded. But then, hadn't she always known that?

They stayed in the French capital for twelve days. For the whole of that time heat and humidity gripped the city like a sweaty fist. But both of them could cope with heat, and the steamy conditions suited the passionate nature of the episode.

Night and day Laura existed in a kind of daze. She'd never really thought of herself as a passionate woman, but Tane had awakened in her a sensuality which, while it shook her, clearly delighted him.

He whispered that she was captivating, irresistible, a fever in his blood, while she lived in a constant state of arousal, her eyes slumbrous, her mouth waiting, her body eager for his possession. She found, as she'd found once before, that he was not only a wonderful, inventive lover, able to bestow the most intense physical pleasure, but also a marvellous companion. There was no sign of the hatred he'd once talked of and, though naturally masterful, he was also thoughtful, considerate and heartbreakingly tender.

Only once did a squall threaten the tropical calm.

On the Friday, they returned from a blissful day spent in the Bois de Boulogne to find a number of flat boxes awaiting them in the sitting-room. Realisation of what the red and gold striped packages contained made Laura's mouth tighten and her cheeks flush with remembered mortification.

She swung round to face Tane, but before she could utter a single word he held up both palms in a gesture of peace and, picking up the phone, asked for the *femme de chambre* who had cleaned their suite that morning to be sent up. Whistling half under his breath, a tune which Laura recognised as "La Marseillaise", he then proceeded to undo the gold bows and take the lids from the various boxes.

When the awaited tap came, he lifted his head and called, *'Entrez!'* The door opened to admit a pretty, appealing young woman with a friendly, open face, which now wore a distinctly worried look.

'Monsieur...madame...' She gave a nervous little bob. 'Is there something wrong?'

'No, nothing's wrong,' Tane assured her. Then, indicating the cheap ring she was wearing, he added, 'As I thought, you're engaged. You're also, to within a couple of centimetres, the same height as Madame, and of a similar build.'

Seeing the girl was looking even more confused and worried, he went on crisply, 'Some things have been delivered which Madame has no use for.' He indicated the open packages. 'She wondered if you would care to have them?'

After gazing at the contents of the boxes as though mesmerised, the girl raised startled eyes. *'All* of them, *monsieur*?'

'All of them,' Tane said firmly.

'Oh, *monsieur*, I...' Without warning, she burst into tears and a flood of French, from which Laura caught only the words, '*merveilleux*' and '*trousseau*'.

'Then they're yours.' Tane rapidly replaced the lids, and piled the boxes into the girl's arms before escorting her to the door.

'*Merci...merci, monsieur... Merci beaucoup, madame...*' She gave Laura a look of awe and gratitude and, as if scarcely daring to believe her good fortune, hurried out.

When Tane had closed the door behind her, Laura remarked, 'That was absurdly generous.'

'Not really. It just seemed a good way of disposing of an embarrassment.' Drily, he added, 'And I've decided I prefer you without clothes.'

On their last morning they had left the hotel and were on their way to the airport when Laura, her fingers touching her bare throat, gave a sudden exclamation.

'What's wrong?' Tane demanded.

'My chain—I've left it behind.'

His shrug dismissed the nine-carat chain as being of little account. 'I'll buy you another one.'

'No...I want that one. Oh, please, Tane...it was David's last gift to me.'

His mouth clamped shut and, the strong bones of his face prominent beneath the tanned skin, he appeared to be fighting some kind of inward battle. Then brusquely he asked the driver to go back.

The chain was still in the bathroom, where Laura had left it, and, radiant with relief, she fastened it around her slender throat.

As Tane watched her, something primitive and ugly flared in his eyes—an expression which was almost instantly masked. When Laura stared at him, wondering if she'd imagined it, he said curtly, 'If we don't hurry we'll miss our plane.'

They flew into London to discover that it too was in the grip of a heat wave. The airport was baking, full of the smell of melting tar and hot metal.

As soon as they had picked up the car, Laura said, 'I'd like to call and see Jamie before we do anything else.' Though she had phoned every day and knew all was well, she was longing to see him.

'Of course,' Tane agreed instantly. 'I was just about to suggest the same thing.'

She was delighted to find the child was as brown as a berry and, as Molly put it, 'As full of beans as an egg's full of meat.'

He'd remembered Tane's promise to take him on a boat, so the three of them went along to the park, where the dry grass was strewn with half-clothed bodies, dogs panted, ice-lollies dripped, and naked toddlers paddled at the water's edge.

For a couple of happy hours it seemed to Laura that Tane was enjoying it as much as she was, as they rowed Jamie round the lake, bought him ice-cream and an orange drink with a bendy straw, and behaved like any other family on a fine Sunday. Then, all too soon, it was time to take him back for his tea, and say goodbye.

As always, parting from her son was a wrench, and Laura was visibly downcast. Before starting the car, Tane took her hand and gave it a comforting squeeze. 'Now we're home you'll be able to see more of him.'

Though delighted by the promise, she knew it wasn't the answer. She ought to be opening the shop, getting on with her life.

Apparently reading her thoughts, Tane said succinctly, 'After four years these few days aren't enough.'

When Monday morning came and she tried to make a stand, he refused point-blank to let her open the shop. However, true to his word, he took her over to see Jamie every single day, and she watched their growing closeness with a feeling she was afraid to acknowledge or identify as hope.

She lived for the next two or three weeks with a feeling of unreality. Though in some ways she was far happier than she'd been for years, it was like an interlude that she knew must end, a holiday that had already gone on too long.

Bills began to come in, bills she refused to let Tane foot, but each one brought her small bank balance lower, and she worried constantly.

Then one night, lying sleepless beside him in bed, she drew the line. If she let things go on like this, with no money coming in, she would soon be entirely dependent on Tane, at his mercy. And wasn't that exactly what he wanted? What he'd wanted from the start?

His breathing was light and even, and she'd thought he was asleep until all at once he asked, 'What is it, Laura? What's bothering you?'

'You know what's bothering me,' she said heavily. 'I owe Molly for taking care of Jamie, the rent's overdue, I've bills to pay and I——'

'I have plenty of money. More than enough to keep you and your son in comfort.'

She gritted her teeth. 'We've been through all this. I can't take money from you.'

'Why not? It's only your pride that stands in the way.'

'I don't want to feel beholden to you. I don't want to be your mistress, your kept woman...'

Quietly, he said, 'If you don't want to be either of those, then marry me. Be my wife.'

CHAPTER EIGHT

LAURA'S heart seemed to pause in its beating, then start again so fast that the blood drummed in her ears. 'Marry you?' It was amazing how even her voice sounded.

'It would be the best way of salving your pride. I take it you would have no objection to my keeping you if you were my wife?'

He was lying quite still, but she could feel the tension in his long, lean body. Slowly, with the utmost care, she said, 'What about Jamie?'

'He appears to be quite happy where he is,' Tane answered in a curiously brittle voice.

Feeling as if she was suffocating, she asked, 'You wouldn't want him with us?'

'You know my feelings about children. I've never wanted my own child. Is it likely I'd want another man's?'

Hope shrivelled and died and was trampled underfoot. So nothing at all had changed.

Tane pushed himself up on one elbow and looked down at her, his face a beautifully sculptured mask in the gloom. 'Well, Laura?'

Her voice cool, controlled, she said, 'No, I won't marry you.'

Equally controlled, he asked, 'Do you mean in those circumstances?'

Disappointment, bitter on her tongue as dead-sea apples, made her say with finality, 'I wouldn't marry you in *any* circumstances.'

134

Abruptly Tane leapt from the bed, and, snatching up his clothes, stormed out of the room. A minute or so later, Laura heard the outer door of the penthouse slam behind him.

The wheel had come full circle.

It was over, she thought with bleak, desolate certainty. Finished. For Jamie's sake she had to find the strength to leave Tane, to pretend that the last few weeks had never happened, and start all over again. But how could she bear the pain that was so much greater this second time? Gazing blindly into the semi-darkness, she lay wide awake until a pink and gold sunrise heralded another lovely day. Then she got up and, moving like a very old woman, pushed her few possessions into her small case.

In the quiet before the Monday morning rush-hour got under way, Laura took the Underground across London. She was in a kind of stupor, weighed down by a leaden despair that was all the heavier because it carried the weight of dead hopes and dreams.

Despite stopping off at the shop to pick up some more of her belongings, she was knocking on Molly's door before nine o'clock. After one look at her ashen face, Molly exclaimed, 'The Lord help us and save us!' Taking the case from Laura's hand and standing it in the passage, she led the way into the kitchen, urging, 'Come and sit down, do.'

The blue and white kettle was starting to whistle and, while she mashed a pot of tea and pushed a steaming cup towards Laura, Molly went on, 'You've just missed Jamie; Anne Masters picked him up early for playschool. But perhaps that's as well. You look as if you need to talk.'

'I need to do more than talk,' Laura said dully. 'I need to find somewhere to stay.'

'You can stay here,' Molly offered with alacrity.

Laura sighed. 'Believe me, I'm grateful, but it has to be somewhere Tane can't find me. Otherwise I would have gone home.'

The older woman pursed her lips. 'Do you want to tell me what's happened?'

'He asked me to marry him, and I refused.'

Obviously thunderstruck, Molly exclaimed, 'Refused? Why on earth——?'

'I *can't* marry him!' Laura said fiercely. 'I told you before, we just aren't...compatible. He doesn't like children.'

'He may not like children *en masse*, but he likes Jamie. I'd stake my life on it. Well, you've seen them together these past weeks...'

Stonily, Laura said, 'He doesn't want Jamie; he said so.'

Molly looked nonplussed. 'Have you told him the child's *his*?'

Laura shook her head. 'But I know it wouldn't make any difference. I *can't* marry him, and I *won't* go on being his mistress. I've got to go somewhere he can't find me, and make a new start.'

'Well, I suppose you know your own mind best.' Molly sounded unconvinced. 'But what will you do about the shop?'

'I'm going to have to leave it closed, at least for the time being, and go right away. But where?'

'I've got the solution!' Molly cried suddenly, excitement making the words tumble over each other. 'I take it the Midlands would be far enough away?'

'The Midlands?'

'You must have heard me talk about Rosie Waters? She married Tom Waters, a cousin of John's, and they moved up to Nottingham. Well, Tom died earlier this year, and Rosie said in her last letter that the house is too big for just her, and she was looking to take a lodger.

'She's part-owner of a hairdressing business, so she's out all day, but when she *is* home she rattles round the house like a solitary grain of rice left in a tin. Would you like me to ring the salon and see what she says?'

Receiving a jerky nod, Molly picked up the extension and dialled Rosie's business number. After a brief explanation, she passed the phone over to Laura.

The voice at the other end was pleasant and friendly, and in a matter of minutes it was arranged that Laura should have, temporarily, at least, a bedroom-cum-sitting-room in the other woman's house.

Rosie rattled off some train times, and gave directions from the Midlands station to Galthorpe Street, where she lived, adding, 'The salon is just around the corner. If you get to Nottingham before five, call in here for the house key. See you later, then. Bye.'

Over another cup of tea, the two women discussed the question of what to do about Jamie. Laura rubbed a hand across her forehead. 'I'll do my utmost to find a job where I can have him with me—perhaps a mother's help or a housekeeper. But if you'll keep him until then...?'

'Of course I will.'

'And if Tane should ask, you won't tell him where I've gone?'

'Wild horses wouldn't drag it out of me——'

A sharp rat-tat at the door made both women jump. They looked at each other wordlessly. After a few seconds the knocking was repeated with a determination that made Molly observe in a whisper, 'I think I'd better answer. If it's Himself, he's not a man to go meekly away. You wait in my bedroom.' Halfway down the passage she turned to point and mouth, 'Don't forget to take your case.'

Laura grabbed the case and, rigid with nervous tension, stood in the neat, squeaky-clean room, and heard Molly open the door and exclaim, 'So it's you, is it?'

Then Tane's deep voice asked, 'Is Laura here yet?'

'No, she isn't,' Molly lied roundly.

'Perhaps I can come in and wait?'

'I'm not expecting her. Jamie's at play-school and I'm off into town myself this very minute.'

Smoothly, Tane suggested, 'If you're going into town, I'll be happy to drop you.'

Sounding not a whit put out, Molly said, 'That's kind of you, so it is.' There was a pause before she added, 'You'd better come in a minute while I get my handbag.'

Listening to the sounds of movement in the kitchen, Laura caught her breath, all at once realising that Molly's little ploy of inviting him in to satisfy him was about to come unstuck.

At the same instant, Tane remarked, 'I see you've had an early visitor.'

'Agnes, my next-door neighbour, popped in for a cup of tea,' Molly explained with just the right amount of casual uninterest. 'She'd probably be here still if I hadn't planned to go out.'

Laura waited motionless until she heard the front door close, the latch of the gate click, and a car start up and drive away. Then, hurrying to the window, she glanced out just in time to see the familiar white Mercedes disappearing up the street. She found she was trembling violently.

Fighting a longing to stay and say goodbye to Jamie, she picked up her case and, banging the door behind her, made her way towards the nearest Tube station.

When, some three quarters of an hour later, she reached St Pancras, she queued up for a sandwich and a cup of coffee, then sat for a long time staring blankly into space while she mulled things over in her mind. Finally, unable to find any reasonable alternative, she bought a ticket and caught an afternoon train to Nottingham.

Having found the salon without difficulty, she went inside and, breathing in the heavily scented atmosphere of perming lotions and shampoo, introduced herself.

Rosie Waters was a woman in her early fifties, plump and vigorous, with bobbed fair hair and a straight fringe above big, gooseberry-pale eyes. Pleasantly, she said, 'I was planning to leave a bit early tonight, so we can go home together.'

'Home' turned out to be a large detached house called Fairmont in a good residential district not far from the river.

Rosie showed Laura into a pleasant bedroom, with a settee and an easy-chair beneath the big bay window, and asked rather diffidently, 'Will this be all right, do you think?' On being assured that it was fine, she added, 'You have your own bathroom next door, but I'm afraid we'll have to share a kitchen. Though truth to tell I do very little cooking these days.'

'About money,' Laura began. 'You'll want some rent in advance and——'

'Not a bit of it,' Rosie broke in cheerfully. 'Stay for a week or two and see how things turn out before you start worrying about rent. I'm eating with friends to-night,' she added, 'so do help yourself to anything you fancy from the fridge or freezer...'

'Do you mind if I use your phone later?' Laura asked. 'I usually call to make sure Jamie's all right.'

'Of course I don't mind. Feel free.'

Laura was in the large, slightly old-fashioned kitchen, preparing a meal of cold meat and salad, which she had no appetite for, when the phone rang. Going through to the living-room, she lifted the receiver and said, 'Hello?'

'I'm just ringing to make sure you arrived all right,' Molly said.

Picking up an odd note in the older woman's voice, Laura demanded, 'Is anything the matter?'

'No, nothing's the matter,' Molly answered.

But still that hint of trouble was there.

'Is Jamie——?'

'Jamie's fine. Though, as you might guess, as soon as I got back from town Himself was on the doorstep. I told him I had to pick the bairn up, so he drove me down.

'When we got back and he mentioned your name I repeated that I wasn't expecting you, that I'd thought you were with *him*.

'It was obvious he didn't believe me, and even more obvious that he had no intention of leaving, so I asked if he'd like to stay for lunch. He said if it wasn't baked beans again he'd be happy to. I went to cut some sandwiches and——'

Why didn't she get to the point? Laura wondered edgily. If there *was* a point.

'—when I got back, Jamie was crayoning happily; but Himself was sitting looking as if the sky had fallen in on top of him. I asked what was wrong. He didn't answer, just looked at me quite blankly, as though he'd suffered a shock that had robbed him of his wits. Then he got up, thanked me very much, but said he wouldn't be staying for lunch, and walked out.'

All this talk of Tane was agony for Laura. Tightly, she asked, 'Is that all?'

'But you didn't see his *face*,' Molly said. 'I only hope he was safe. He got into that posh car of his and drove off like someone in a trance.' As if suddenly realising she might be worrying Laura, she added more brightly, 'But I dare say he'll be all right, and I've no doubt that, when he realises you're *really* gone, he'll be back. As I remarked once before, he isn't a man to give up easily...'

Before Molly rang off she put Jamie on as usual.

'Are you listening, darling?' Laura said. 'Mummy can't get to see you for a while, but I'll come as soon as I can, I promise. Night and God bless, now. Be a good boy...'

Jamie mumbled something she didn't catch.

'What, darling? Say that again.'

The mumble was repeated, then she heard Molly in the background obviously answering Jamie. 'I don't know, we'll have to wait and see, pet.' Then to Laura, 'He wanted to know if *he* will be coming... Now, then, don't you worry about ringing every night. *I'll* phone you.'

Laura found it necessary to summon all her reserves of strength to get through the endless hours that followed without giving way to despair. Leaving Tane had made her feel as if a vital part of herself had been torn away and she was slowly bleeding to death. To that was added the worry that Jamie too might miss him.

But a core of common sense told her it had been the right decision, a decision she would have been forced to take sooner or later, and delaying would only have made the inevitable parting worse for both herself and Jamie.

Pushing everything to the back of her mind, she spent the next day job-hunting, without success. Though quite a number of people were advertising for a housekeeper, none was willing to take a woman with a young child.

When Molly rang that evening the news did nothing to cheer her. 'Himself was back this morning looking as if he hadn't slept for a week and the devil was at his heels,' Molly reported. 'He demanded to know where you were. I said I'd no idea, and he said, "Come off it," very politely.

'Then he asked if you were all right. He seemed genuinely worried. I said I hadn't heard from you, and he said, "But of course if you do, you'll let me know," and I said, "Of course..."'

Laura was still untangling this skein of words when Molly got her second wind and carried on, 'He left then, but I noticed one nondescript little man was watching the house, and another following me everywhere I went.'

So Tane had hired detectives.

'I'm sorry,' Laura muttered helplessly.

'Don't you go worrying yourself about it,' Molly said stoutly. 'It doesn't bother me. I'm leading them a merry dance, so I am.' She sounded as if she was thoroughly enjoying all the excitement and intrigue. 'We had a sudden downpour this evening, so I took the one across the road an umbrella and told him I hoped for his sake that it wouldn't be long before the night-shift turned up. You should have seen his face!'

The next two days passed with still no job in sight, and Laura was feeling more depressed than ever when the phone rang that evening.

'Tane's just left,' Molly told her. 'He said to give you an ultimatum. Either you come back to him at once, or he'll take whatever action he thinks is necessary to bring you back.'

'I should have expected this,' Laura burst out bitterly. 'The only reason he bought the Lulworth building was to give him a hold over me. He admitted as much.'

'If it'll help I'll lend you the money for the quarter's rent,' Molly offered.

'That's marvellous of you.' Laura was touched. 'But he doesn't really want the rent. If I paid that he'd think of something else.'

'So what will you do?' Molly asked.

'Ignore his ultimatum and leave the ball in his court, the arrogant brute!'

Laura found a healthy dose of anger was better than the bleak misery she'd been struggling with for days.

On Sunday night a heavy thunderstorm finally broke the heat wave, and Monday dawned cool and clear. Her luck seemed to have changed with the weather. A businessman who was looking for a housekeeper for six months while his wife was abroad agreed that if the child was no trouble he'd be prepared to give the arrangement a try.

By lunchtime Laura was making her way back to Fairmont feeling relieved and almost jubilant. She'd barely got in when the phone started to ring. Molly was on the other end sounding panic-stricken, almost incoherent. 'Laura? Oh, dear Lord, I don't know how to tell you...'

Laura had a sudden clear vision of Tane lying in the mangled wreckage of his car, dying, perhaps dead... He'd reacted so violently the last time she'd left him, and, though this time the fuel was hate rather than love, the feeling it engendered was just as intense... But in her blind selfishness she'd thought only of Jamie and herself. Not of *him*. Never of *him*.

Through the shock and fear she became aware that Molly was still talking. '... and when the bairn was nowhere to be seen she didn't know what to do for the best...'

Her brain suddenly cool and lucid, Laura ordered, 'Start from the beginning and tell me plainly. Has something happened to Jamie?'

There was a sound like a gulp, then Molly said, 'Anne was supposed to collect him from play-school and bring him home, then she and the children were going to stay for lunch. But a few minutes ago she rang up, dreadfully upset.

'It seems they'd just got outside when Mark fell down and grazed his knee. Anne picked him up and wiped the blood away, and when she turned round, Jamie, who'd been standing quietly beside Becky's push-chair, had vanished.

'She thought at first he'd gone back inside for something, but when she looked he wasn't there, and she can't find him anywhere...' Molly's voice had risen to a wail.

'Have you told the police?' Laura asked urgently.

'Not yet, but I will. Are you——?'

'I'm coming. I'll be there as soon as possible.'

Shaking like a leaf, Laura depressed the receiver and dialled the local taxi firm. After scrawling a few lines to Rosie, she snatched up her bag and hurried outside to wait for the cab, and by sheer good fortune it got her to the station just minutes before the London train was due to depart.

The forced inactivity of the journey was a nightmare, and she sat icy cold and tense, trying not to think of all the dreadful possibilities, but still drowning in the well of her own fears. Jamie had been warned not to take sweets from, or go with, anyone he didn't know, but he was as naturally friendly and trusting as a young puppy.

Oh, please God, Laura prayed silently, keep him safe; don't let anything happen to him. He's only a baby...

Apparently responding to her mental urging, the train drew into St Pancras a little early. Before the wheels had stopped moving, she was out of the carriage and almost running down the platform.

As she hurried to get a taxi, a white Mercedes swung into the kerb and a man leaped out. She looked into that dark, powerful face, and burst into tears.

'Don't cry,' Tane said urgently. 'Please don't cry.' He gathered her close, cradling her head against his chest. 'It's all right...everything's all right.'

'Jamie——'

'Jamie's fine.' When she continued to sob, he shook her. 'Listen to me. *Jamie is all right.* He's safe in my office. I'm taking you to him now.'

But, completely overwrought, Laura was unable to stop crying, though now it was with relief rather than fear.

With an arm around her shoulders, he hurried her into the car and, getting in beside her, reached over to fasten her seatbelt. Before starting the engine, he shook out a folded handkerchief and put it into her hand.

While she mopped at the still flowing tears and blew her nose, Tane said, 'I'm sorry for the way things have turned out. I didn't intend to give you all this worry.'

Light began to dawn. She recalled the ultimatum Molly had passed on: 'Either you come back to him at once or he'll take whatever action he thinks is necessary to bring you back.'

Anger would come later, but just at that moment she felt too wrung out to be capable of any further emotion. Jamie was safe, and that was all that mattered. She spoke carefully. 'I know you're a ruthless devil, but I never dreamt you meant to do anything so...' Her voice wobbled and she bit her lip before going on. 'How *could* you terrify poor Anne Masters and Molly the way you did?'

'I'm sorry about that,' Tane admitted, 'but things went wrong. Look, we need to stop and talk.'

He swung the wheel round and headed for Hyde Park. Once through the gates, he drew smoothly into the first available parking space and, switching off the engine, turned towards her.

She studied him, as though detailing his features for the first time. The long-lashed eyes beneath dark, level brows, the straight nose and strong bone-structure, the well-shaped mouth and firm jaw. But no factual description could convey the power and magnetism of that face.

Tane gave a short, sharp sigh. 'If everything had gone according to plan, no one would have had any reason to panic...

'It was my intention to pick Jamie up a shade early— I'd been to the school so many times that the staff knew me well—and leave a note for Molly, explaining what I'd done.'

'So what went wrong?' Laura asked coldly.

'At the last minute I was held up. When I got there the place was milling with people, and I thought I was too late. I couldn't see any sign of Molly, but suddenly I caught sight of Jamie. At the same instant he spotted me and came running over.

'He was more than happy to come with me so, while I got him settled in the car, Lola—do you remember Lola Ashton, my secretary?—took my note into school and asked if one of the staff would give it to Mrs Seaton as soon as she arrived.

'When I got back to my office, I rang Molly to make sure she'd read the note and was going to get in touch with you. That was when I realised things had come unstuck. Thinking Jamie had disappeared, she'd already spoken to you.

'She told me where you were and gave me your phone number. I tried immediately to get through, but I'd missed you. I left Lola and Jamie entertaining one another, and went to apologise to Molly and Mrs Masters for giving them such a fright.'

'And I suppose they forgave you?' The resentment was evident.

'I hope so,' he said soberly.

'Molly was going to call the police,' Laura remembered.

'Luckily I was just in time to stop her.'

'*I* could still do it.'

His gaze clear and level, he asked, 'What would you tell them? You thought your son was missing, but now you've found he's safe with his father?'

Laura sat perfectly still, transfixed, while every trace of colour drained from her face. Unconsciously tugging at the gold chain, she began, 'What makes you think——?'

'I don't *think*. I *know*. Last Monday I was at Molly's and, while she went to get lunch ready, Jamie showed me his crayoning book. At the play-school that morning they'd been learning to write their names.

'His letters were wobbly and all different sizes, as you might expect, but it was still quite easy to read "James Tane". So I did some checking.

'Jamie's birthday isn't June the sixth. He was born on March the sixth at the Fulgrove Maternity Hospital. *He's my son and you never told me.*' Softly, Tane added, 'He must have been conceived that very first time.'

'I'm sure he was,' Laura agreed bitterly. 'After that you were very careful to take precautions.'

Tane's beautifully sculptured mouth hardened. 'Did Belmont know the child wasn't his?'

'Yes, he knew,' she said steadily. 'That was one of the reasons he asked me to marry him.'

'That and the fact that he'd always wanted you. How *could* you marry another man when you were carrying my child?'

'Can you blame me?' she flared. 'You said no children. What did you want me to do when I discovered I was pregnant—crawl back so you could make me have an abortion?'

He flinched as though she'd struck him. 'I would never have done that. Being a father——'

'You may be Jamie's father,' Laura broke in, 'but he's *my* son. You never wanted him——'

'I want him now.' Tane's voice was dangerously quiet.

'You don't want *him*, you just want a weapon to use against me. You want——'

'I want you to marry me.'

'Well, I won't.' Her small, heart-shaped face was white and set; she looked as stubborn as any mule.

'Oh, I think you will. You see, if you don't, I'll take Jamie away from you.'

'You can't do that!' she cried. 'I'm his mother, and I——'

'A mother who can't afford to support him. Who can't even have him with her. I'm in a much better position to keep and educate him.'

'I'll fight you every step of the way,' she told him fiercely. 'And these days a court will nearly always come down on the mother's side.'

Watching her like a hawk, he said, 'Unless that mother can be shown to be unfit to keep a child.'

'Unfit...?' She felt the beginnings of real fear.

'It's no use fighting me. I have money and, where you're concerned, not too many scruples. If, for example, your ex-landlord stated he's seen undesirable men coming to the shop...'

Laura stared at him, her deep blue eyes wide and incredulous in her stricken face.

'For pity's sake, don't look like that,' he said roughly. 'I don't want to have to play dirty, but I will if you force me.'

And he would.

She realised now that marrying her was what he'd intended, what he'd *planned* from the start, and, with relative speed and ease, and utter ruthlessness, he'd got her exactly where he wanted her. Head bent, she looked down at her clenched hands.

He used a finger to tilt her chin, and she saw from his expression that the mood of cruelty had passed and there was a new gentleness in him.

'Previously you've refused to marry me on my terms,' he said slowly. 'So this time I'll allow *you* to make the terms.'

It was a telling concession.

He took a familiar box from his pocket and slipped her engagement-ring on to her finger as though it was settled, and the fact that she made no move to stop him seemed to prove it was.

'Would you like to tell me your terms?'

'I haven't any *terms*,' she said, her voice coming from a long way off. 'I just want to have Jamie with me, and an equal say in deciding his future.'

'You once told me that when we had children you'd like a house in the country with a real garden. Wouldn't you still?'

'Well, yes, but——'

'Then you can start looking for something suitable as soon as we get back from our honeymoon. Anything else?'

As she began to shake her head, he suggested, 'Perhaps you'd like me to sire another half a dozen children?'

Laura flushed scarlet. 'No, I wouldn't. I believe children need a happy, stable background.'

His smoky eyes lit. 'And you don't think we could provide that?'

'Tane...' It was a plea. 'Are you *sure* you want this? Isn't a forced marriage just storing up heartache and misery for both of us?'

'A lifetime's penance?' he suggested. She said nothing, her face open, defenceless. 'It isn't ideal,' he admitted after a moment. 'But it's better than no marriage at all.'

But was it? What if they ended up destroying each other?

A fresh thought struck her. 'You won't...won't use Jamie to get at me, will you?'

'If I say I won't, do you trust me?'

'Yes.' And oddly enough she did.

She stared at the beautiful diamond starburst on her finger, and wondered if such a marriage had any chance of succeeding. Despite everything, she loved him, but she scarcely knew whether it would bring more pain to live *with* him than *without* him.

It seemed incredible that only a few hours ago she'd been in another city, trying to forget him and start a new life, feeling she'd never be whole again.

He took her face between his palms. 'Perhaps a kiss to seal the bargain? Then we should pick up our son and tell Molly the good news.'

Our son. The bitter-sweet words made her eyes fill with tears, tears which spilt over as his lips touched hers.

His kiss was light but lingering. When he lifted his head he gazed down at her with a look that could have been mistaken for tenderness, and wiped away her tears with his thumbs.

CHAPTER NINE

BY THE time they reached Carlson Holdings, the staff were leaving for the night, coming out in ones and twos, or descending the steps in chattering groups. Some of them were unfamiliar, but a considerable number Laura recognised. She had been well liked, and now she found herself answering quite a few surprised and pleased hellos.

'By the way,' Tane said, as they went up in the lift, 'all I told Lola was that I was picking up your son from play-school. Being no fool, she might have guessed there was a little more to it than that, but she'll keep it to herself.'

It was over four years since Laura had been up to the top floor of the building, but it could have been yesterday. Trying not to let past memories swamp her, she allowed Tane to shepherd her along the corridor and into his office.

Jamie was sitting at Lola's desk on a swivel-chair raised to its highest extent, a tray with an empty plate and half a tumbler of milk by his elbow. A jumper, several sheets of paper with crayoned 'pictures' and letters, a light-weight duffel bag, and a small pair of canvas shoes were strewn across the carpet.

The middle-aged woman and the child were so intent on a computer game, which seemed to involve a variety of bizarre animals and miniature green men, that neither noticed the door open. Only when Laura and Tane

152

moved further into the room did the pair look up simultaneously.

'Mummy!' Jamie was off the chair in an instant and flying across the room.

Feeling such a rush of maternal love that it hurt, Laura stooped and caught him in her arms, hugging the squirming little body to her so hard that Jamie complained, 'You're quashing me, Mummy!'

She laughed shakily. 'I'm sorry, darling.'

Her lovely eyes still full of emotion, she glanced up to find Tane watching her. For an unguarded moment his face showed both remorse and longing, and a kind of shamefaced jealousy—a sad mixture of emotions that tore her heart and reminded her only too clearly of what she'd suffered during her empty, loveless childhood. But before she could even stretch out her hand to him he turned away, his expression becoming cool and businesslike.

'Come an' look...come an' look...' Entranced by his new toy, Jamie began dragging her towards the computer. Having noticed he had jam and biscuit crumbs around his mouth, and his fingers were sticky, she said hastily, 'Don't touch anything.'

'I *got* to touch,' he explained, 'we're playing a game.'

'It's all right, really,' Lola assured her.

Laura gave the other woman a grateful smile. 'Thank you very much for taking care of him. I hope he hasn't been too much of a handful?'

'Not at all. He's a delightful child—so happy and friendly.'

'How is your mother keeping now?' Laura asked, then instantly wished she hadn't. Four years was a long time, and something might have happened to the older woman.

But Lola was smiling, answering, 'Very well. She has some special therapy twice a week, which eases the pain, and now we have a live-in nurse-companion, which means she's not left alone while I'm out at work.' The grateful glance she cast in Tane's direction made it abundantly clear who had provided those benefits.

'Look!' Jamie tugged at Laura's skirt, directing her attention to the screen. As soon as she was obediently looking, he scrambled down from his perch again and, trotting over to Tane, who had gone to sit at his own desk, took his hand. '*You* got to come an' look too.'

It struck Laura that, for someone who had no fondness for children, Tane seemed to be more pleased than annoyed at being included.

While the child's dark head and the woman's iron-grey one bent in concentration, they watched until, amid much excitement, all the little green men had been gobbled up, the game ended, and the computer was shut down.

After giving Lola some brief instructions for the following day, Tane thanked her. Then Jamie, his arms round her neck, bestowed on her a smacking kiss which, being as spontaneous as it was sticky, obviously delighted her.

When Lola had collected her belongings and set off for home, Tane remarked, 'I must check up on Aunt Beatrice before we leave. She had a fall earlier today, and they've taken her to Yawton cottage hospital.' Answering Laura's unspoken question, he added, 'That was the phone call which made me late getting to playschool.'

As he dialled the number, Laura took Jamie through to the cloakroom, and tried to keep him still long enough to wash his face and hands and run a comb through his unruly dark curls.

On her return she found Tane just replacing the receiver. He looked concerned and, though he'd never actually said so, she felt sure he had a great deal of affection for his aunt.

'How are things?' she asked.

'There are no broken bones, but she hit her head on the stone floor of the kitchen, and hasn't yet recovered consciousness. They say her condition is stable, however.'

Less than five minutes later they had joined the streams of traffic and were battling through the evening rush-hour on their way to Molly's.

She was on the doorstep to greet them, giving Jamie a hug that showed just how worried she'd been. As he scampered inside, she threw her arms around Laura. 'You poor thing, you must have had an awful fright. Are you all right?'

'Yes, I'm fine,' Laura said resolutely. 'I'm only sorry you and Anne were so worried.'

'Oh, well, everything's fine now, and it's no use making a flagpole out of a matchstick. All the same——' Molly gave Tane a scathing glance '—the man's an idjit, so he is.'

Laura gave a little choke of laughter, and felt some of the tension ease.

'Come in, do,' Molly urged. 'You'll stay for tea, won't you? I've been baking all afternoon. I find cooking useful for taking my mind off things.' While they ate their way through sausage rolls, quiche, buttered scones, tarts, and cake, and drank several cups of tea, she asked, 'So, would you mind telling me, what's the situation?'

Tane's white, healthy teeth had just bitten through a scone, and he chewed and swallowed before answering,

'We're getting married as soon as possible. I don't see any point in disturbing Jamie's routine until it's necessary, so if it's all right with you I'd like things to stay as they are until we get back from our honeymoon.'

'A honeymoon, is it? Well, now!'

'What's anunimoon?' Jamie asked through a large bite of sausage roll.

'Haven't I told you repeatedly not to talk with your mouth full?' Molly scolded him lovingly.

'A honeymoon is a holiday two people take together after they're married,' Tane told him.

'What's mawwied?'

'Married is when a man and a woman promise to live together and look after one another all their lives.'

'Like Mark's mummy and daddy,' Molly added to the explanation.

Jamie leaned against Tane's knee, and sucked his thumb thoughtfully. 'Are *you* going to look after *my* mummy?'

'I'm going to try.'

'An' look after me?'

'I certainly am.'

'Will that make you be my daddy?'

Tane hesitated, and glanced at Laura.

'He *is* your daddy,' she said quietly. 'He's *always* been your daddy, only we...we weren't able to live together. Now we will be able to.'

With the acceptance of the very young, Jamie only asked, 'Can I have a bruvver, then?'

'We'll see what we can do,' Tane promised lazily.

Recalling his sardonic, 'Perhaps you'd like me to sire another half a dozen children?' Laura felt a fierce stab of pain.

'Will Auntie Molly live wiv us?' Jamie wanted to know.

'No, I won't be living with you. I have my own home,' Molly pointed out.

Seeing them both look gloomy, Tane suggested to Jamie, 'Tell you what. As you don't have a grannie of your own, if you ask nicely, Auntie Molly may agree to be your very special grannie.'

'What's a gwannie?'

When that had been duly explained, Jamie turned to Molly and asked seriously, '*Will* you?'

'That I will, pet,' she told him, her eyes suspiciously bright. Turning to Laura, she went on briskly, 'I almost forgot—Rosie rang up. She'd found your note, and was very concerned. I told her it had all been a mistake, and you'd get in touch with her later on.'

Recalling how very kind the other woman had been, Laura said, 'I'll give her a call now, if you don't mind?'

'Of course I don't mind. She'll be glad to hear the good news, so she will.'

There had been no chance of a private talk with Molly, and what was there to say? The older woman clearly believed that, through Tane's determination, love had triumphed, and it was no use worrying her by revealing just what lengths he had gone to to get his way.

'Married? Bless me!' Rosie exclaimed, when Laura had got through to the Nottingham number. 'Well, I *am* pleased. Though of course I'll be sorry to lose your company. You won't be coming back, I take it? What do you want me to do about your things?'

Tane, who had been listening, said, 'Ask her to keep them until we know the exact day we're getting married. If she can get to the wedding, I'll send a car down for her.'

Having relayed this, Laura heard Rosie's squeal of excitement. 'What a marvellous reason for buying a new outfit!'

At Molly's invitation they stayed on to supervise Jamie's bath. Though Tane took no active part, lounging, hands in pockets, against the door-jamb, he watched with benevolent interest.

Jamie, clearly delighted by the male presence, chattered non-stop, and insisted on Tane tucking him into bed, helping him with his prayers, and kissing a varied and battered collection of stuffed animals.

Watching them together, Laura felt the cold, tight knot in her chest begin to loosen. Surely Jamie would benefit from having a father? But what if Tane, having got his way, resented the child, and showed it?

No, he wouldn't *show* it, at least not in front of Jamie, she was quite certain of that. His own childhood having been spoilt by a father who hadn't wanted him, he wouldn't let it happen to *his* son.

When they finally said goodbye to Molly and drove back to the penthouse, Laura went with very mixed feelings. Having spent a long, long week away from Tane, part of her yearned to be in his arms, but her independent spirit was still angry and indignant over his threats and his autocratic treatment.

On arriving home—strangely enough she now thought of it as home—Tane asked, 'Do you want anything else to eat tonight?'

She shook her head. 'I'm ready for bed.'

'Ah...' he said softly, and gave her a glittering glance from beneath thick, dark lashes.

His casual male arrogance, his certainty that, despite everything, she would sleep with him, brought all Laura's resentment flooding to the surface.

When he took her in his arms and bent to kiss her, despising herself for wanting him so, she stiffened and turned away, fingering the gold chain around her neck.

Laura heard the hiss of breath drawn through his teeth. There was a moment's calm before the storm, then, taking her chin, he wrenched her head round and kissed her mercilessly, grinding her soft inner lip against her teeth until she tasted blood. She began to resist, to fight against the pressure of his arms and mouth.

Subduing her struggles, he carried her into the bedroom and threw her on to the bed, then, handling her with a careless strength that verged on brutality, he stripped off her clothes.

Knowing how futile resistance was, she made no further attempt to fight him, but lay limp and shivering, her head turned away, while his hands moved over her bare flesh. When she continued to lie quite still, his fingers gentled and paused, a palm cupped her cheek and turned her face towards him. 'Look at me, Laura.'

'I don't want to look at you,' she said, very low. 'I never want to see you again. I *hate* you.'

The hand was withdrawn, and a moment later she heard the door close.

She hadn't meant it. Of course she hadn't meant it, and, if he'd displayed any kindness, the slightest degree of tenderness, she wouldn't have been able to hold out against him. But all he'd shown her was his arrogance and determination.

Shaking and miserable, she crept beneath the duvet and, drawing up her knees, curled into a protective ball.

Laura slept in fits and starts, and awoke next morning feeling dismal and unrefreshed, reluctant to face both the day and Tane's wrath. When she had showered and pulled on her clothes, she squared her shoulders and went through to the living-room to find him just replacing the phone.

'I've been on to the hospital again,' he informed her coldly. 'Beatrice still hasn't regained consciousness. I've told them I'm going up.' His blue-grey eyes were sunken and his strong face looked tired, as if he'd had very little sleep.

Laura's hostility softened and melted into compassion. It would be a long, lonely journey, and there might be bad news awaiting him. Obeying a sudden impulse, she asked, 'Would you like me to go with you?' Before she could begin to decipher the intense expression which crossed his face, it was gone.

Deliberately offhand, he answered, 'If you want to. But I was intending to start straight away.'

'I'm ready,' she informed him quietly.

'You haven't had any breakfast,' he pointed out.

She took a gamble. 'Have you?'

'No.'

With a waiting expression on her face, she said nothing.

He shrugged. 'OK, let's go. We'll have a bite to eat on the way up.'

They talked very little on the lengthy drive, Laura alternately dozing and looking out of the window. But still, she was *there*; he wasn't alone.

Just beyond Doncaster they stopped at an old coaching inn to get a bite to eat. Though they wasted no time, it was late afternoon before they reached Yawton.

Even in bright sunshine the small market town had the somewhat dour, windswept look of many north-eastern places. Its grey stone cottages and church, its school, shops, and various pubs all stood four-square and sturdy, with the wild moors laying siege right up to their back doors.

They arrived at the hospital, which was on the outskirts of Yawton, to find good news awaiting them. Beatrice had recovered consciousness earlier in the day.

'Dr Meadows is with Miss Waldon now,' the short, plump nurse informed them, as she led the way to a sunny side-room off the main ward.

Wearing a red flannel dressing-gown and a determined expression, Beatrice was sitting in a chair by the bed, alert and cantankerous, demanding of a young, harassed-looking doctor that she should be sent home forthwith. She was dark-haired and wiry, and looked younger than her years, though her fingers and joints were swollen and knobbly with arthritis.

Tane bent and kissed the still pale cheek. 'How are you feeling?'

'I'm fine.' Testily she added, 'I couldn't believe it when they told me you were coming. Fancy trailing all this way to see an old woman!' While Beatrice was talking her shrewd eyes were assessing Laura, taking note of the engagement-ring.

'This is Laura Belmont, my future wife,' Tane told her briefly. 'Now what's all this nonsense about wanting to go home?'

'Hospitals are only for sick folks,' Beatrice insisted. 'There's nothing wrong with me. All I did was trip over a mat, and my head's like iron.'

'It certainly seems to be,' the doctor agreed with a grin. 'There's no sign of a fracture or other cranial damage.'

'Then what is there to stop me going home?' she demanded.

'In any blow to the head there may be some delayed effects...'

'Delayed effects my foot!' Beatrice snorted. 'If you think I'm going to stay here for days while you wait for delayed effects...'

The two men exchanged speaking glances.

'But living alone as you do...' the doctor tried again.

'I don't live alone,' she said firmly, 'Percy lives with me...' Dr Meadows looked confused '...and, though I understand my neighbour is feeding him, he's sure to miss me.'

'Percy's your dog?'

'My cat, and I refuse to leave him on his own to fret...'

'What if I make arrangements for Miss Waldon to have a resident nurse for a few days?' Tane put in.

Breathing an undisguised sigh of relief, the doctor suggested, 'Perhaps you'd like to come next door to the office?'

When the two men had gone, Laura, who had taken an instant liking to Beatrice, smiled at the elderly woman and asked, 'I understand you live in Yawton?'

'Yes; I was born in the old family house next to the church, and I've lived there all my life.' Beatrice indicated one of the uncomfortable-looking metal chairs arrayed by the wall. 'Why don't you sit down?'

Laura obediently pulled one of the chairs forward, and sat. There was a short silence, then the older woman asked abruptly, 'Has your name always been Belmont?'

'No,' Laura answered quietly, 'my maiden name was Peters.'

The grey eyes watching her hardened. 'Though I've never met you, I thought I recognised you from Tane's description and some photographs he once showed me...

'When you walked out on him last time, he was shattered. I don't want to see him hurt again.'

'Neither do I.' Feeling she needed to reassure this blunt, down-to-earth woman who had looked after the young Tane with such undemonstrative kindness, Laura said simply, 'I love him. I've always loved him.'

'So he wasn't the only one to get hurt? What went wrong? Tane's never spoken about it, and I've often wondered.'

'I wanted a family. He didn't.'

There was a long pause, then Beatrice said slowly, 'Simple words for such a complicated situation.'

'It was more complicated even than that. Though neither of us knew it, when I left Tane I was carrying his baby.'

'Oh, dear God,' Beatrice muttered. 'You didn't...?'

'No, I didn't. I had a childhood friend who had asked me several times to marry him. When he found I was pregnant, he asked me again, and I accepted.'

'Did things work out? Were you happy with him?'

How could she have been happy? She'd missed Tane every minute of every hour of every day. Each night she'd dreamt of him, trying to hold him close, to keep him with her, but every time he'd walked away, and she'd wakened with tears still wet on her cheeks.

But now she answered matter-of-factly, 'As happy as it was possible to be in the circumstances. David treated Tane's son like his own. He was a wonderful person, and I loved him very dearly.'

'Was?'

'He died over a year ago from a rare form of pernicious anaemia.'

'And the boy?'

'Jamie's a happy, extrovert child, who's going to be very like Tane.'

Beatrice's grey eyes suddenly looked over-bright and her voice was gruff as she asked, 'When are you two getting married?'

'As soon as possible, Tane said. Though I can still hardly believe it. Things have happened so fast since we met again and he found out about Jamie.'

'You said he didn't want children, but I take it he does want his son?'

'He says he does. But I'm so afraid he might not,' Laura admitted unhappily. 'With him believing *he* broke up his parents' marriage——'

'What?' Beatrice looked startled.

'He told me how his mother wanted children but his father didn't, and——'

'So that's what she made him believe!' Beatrice exclaimed. 'Though I never talked to Tane about it—I thought it was best forgotten—I knew she'd done her best to poison his mind against his father... But it wasn't like that at all. And as for an innocent child breaking up their marriage...! It was her own nature that did that.

'I knew my sister better than anyone else in the world, and I loved her dearly, but it didn't blind me to her faults. Diane was as beautiful as a butterfly, but vain and utterly selfish. In her whole life she never loved anyone but herself, and she used sex as a weapon, or in exchange for the things she wanted. And she wanted Mike Carlson.

'Mike was well-off; unfortunately for him he was also besotted with her. He gave her everything her avaricious little heart desired—she used to write and tell me all about it—and for a while the marriage seemed to be working.

'But he was a man with a growing business empire, and he wanted a son to follow in his footsteps. After waiting patiently for quite a number of years, he put his foot down and *insisted*. Diane didn't want children, but she didn't want to lose Mike, and what his money could buy, so reluctantly she agreed.

'From then on neither of them knew a moment's happiness. She *hated* being pregnant, *hated* spoiling her figure, *hated* what she called "the pain and ugliness of childbirth".

'She never forgave Mike for forcing it on her, and, after she realised he thought a lot more of his son than he did of her, she became insanely jealous. When they finally reached the end of the road, although she didn't want Tane, she took him with her to spite Mike...'

Laura glanced up to find Tane standing motionless in the doorway. At the same moment Beatrice saw him and asked, 'So how much did you overhear?'

'Enough.'

'Well, I'm glad you know the truth of the matter at last.'

Tane shrugged. 'It's illuminating, but no longer relevant.' Striding over to the window, he stood for a few seconds looking out across the neatly kept lawns and flower-beds before turning to say, 'We're staying overnight. I've booked a couple of rooms for Laura and myself at the Shoulder of Mutton.

'Dr Meadows has agreed that, all being well, we can take you home tomorrow morning, when a private nurse will be available. She'll stay until the hospital are satisfied that there are no problems.'

Beatrice grunted.

Tane grinned briefly. 'I want to make sure you're well enough to come to the wedding.'

'I'll be well enough for that,' she promised.

* * *

On a calm, golden morning in early October, Laura and
Tane were married very quietly at St Jude's. By mutual
agreement, Jamie was spending the day with Anne
Masters, and looking forward to a family outing to the
zoo.

Only four guests were present at the ceremony: Molly,
who was resplendent in a greeny blue suit and a hat with
iridescent feathers, and Aunt Beatrice, Rosie, and Lola
Ashton, all similarly dressed up to the hilt.

Lola's elder brother, Maurice, a good-looking man in
his fifties, gave Laura away, and Julian Shaw, a friend
and business colleague of Tane's, was best man.

The whole party had dined together the previous
evening, and got along famously. Julian, a slim, dark
man with steady brown eyes and a nice smile, had divided
his attention between Rosie, Beatrice, and Lola, while
Maurice and Molly had hit it off from the word go,
chattering and laughing together like a pair of teenagers.

Discovering by chance that Maurice was a widower,
Laura had crossed her fingers and hoped the instant attraction might develop into something more permanent.

After dinner was over, Tane had driven Laura and
Molly back to Ealing. Laura was staying the night at the
older woman's house in order to leave from there next
morning. As soon as the car had drawn into the kerb,
Molly had jumped out and hurried indoors, leaving
Laura and Tane still in their seats. When Laura would
have reached for the door-handle, Tane's fingers had
closed around her wrist and kept her there.

'The groom's present to the bride.' He tossed a soft
grey leather case into her lap.

She opened it and saw, by the dashboard light, a
gleaming string of beautifully matched ivory pearls. 'I
haven't anything to give you,' she said in a very low voice.

'You can give me everything I'll ever want or need.' His voice was harsh. He came round and, having opened her door, helped her out. It was a lovely evening, with a clear indigo sky and a warm breeze blowing the stars about.

Standing beside him in the darkness, tendrils of hair brushing her cheek like a lover's caress, Laura waited, but he made no move to kiss her.

'Goodnight, then.' Voice muffled, head bent, she opened the gate and followed Molly into the house.

Standing in a quiet backwater in Kensington, the small grey church of St Jude's was very old and sadly neglected, its once glorious stained-glass windows dusty and dim as near-sightless eyes.

Composed, but pale, after a night spent tossing and turning restlessly, Laura walked up the aisle on Maurice Ashton's arm. She was dressed in a calf-length dress of ivory silk with a matching jacket, and carried a spray of creamy rosebuds starred with gypsophilia. She was wearing very little make-up, the merest gloss of pink lipstick and a touch of mascara, and her sun-streaked hair curled loosely on to her shoulders. Her only jewellery was the lustrous string of pearls Tane had given her.

The vicar, gaunt and balding, with large, bony hands and a voice which seemed too deep and sonorous for his narrow chest, gave her an encouraging smile.

But throughout the service Laura shivered, beset by a combination of nerves and the dank coolness of the church. Repeatedly her gaze was drawn to the man standing motionless by her side. It was as if she no longer knew him, as if he'd taken on all the attributes of a handsome stranger.

Dressed in a well-cut pearl-grey suit, a white carnation in his buttonhole, his peat-dark hair shorter than usual

and brushed back from his high forehead, Tane looked
austere, his lean face, with its high cheekbones and
beautifully chiselled mouth, coolly aloof.

That day in the hospital, when he had told Beatrice
he'd booked two rooms at the Shoulder of Mutton, it
had been the exact truth. Having escorted Laura upstairs, he had bidden her a coldly civil goodnight, and
left her at her door. And since their return from
Northumberland he hadn't once kissed her, nor had he
touched her except when it was unavoidable.

He'd returned to his business, going into the office
every day and working late most evenings, and, with no
word of explanation, he had moved into the guest-room
to sleep.

On the rare occasions they were together, he had
treated her with a studied politeness that chilled and
distanced her, making her glad to spend most of her time
at Molly's.

Laura had thought a great deal about the light Beatrice
had shed on his childhood, and wondered what he'd
meant by saying it was 'no longer relevant'. If things
hadn't been so strained she would have broached the
subject, but, tongue-tied by his cool reserve, she hadn't
felt able to ask him.

Each Saturday and Sunday he had driven her over to
Molly's so they could spend the whole day with Jamie.
Feeling she owed it to both of them to let them *really*
get to know one another, she had left them alone together
as much as possible.

She would have been only too delighted by their obvious pleasure in each other's company if Tane hadn't
seemed to draw a circle that shut her out. She wondered
again, as she'd wondered frequently during the past

weeks, if he still wanted her. Or if, after branding himself on her very soul, his passion for her had died.

But, if it had, why was he going through with this wedding? Was it because of Jamie? Because he doubted her ability to care for the child on her own? Or because he genuinely wanted his son?

In spite of his coldness, his deliberate withdrawal, in spite of all her doubts and worries as to what the future held, she *yearned* for him, *ached* for him. Her pride, even her sense of self-preservation, were as nothing when weighed against what she felt for this man.

She knew now that, even if she could never have his love, if he still wanted her she would live with him on almost any terms rather than live without him.

CHAPTER TEN

LEAVING the vault-like gloom of the church for the warm brightness outside was blinding. Catching the toe of her ivory court shoe against a raised paving-stone, Laura stumbled, and Tane caught her arm and tucked it through his own.

Laughing and joking, the wedding party strolled to the nearby Park Hamilton for a sumptuous lunch. Though small, it was a lively gathering, the atmosphere festive. If Laura was a bit quiet, no one appeared to notice. Tane seemed to have thrown off his sombre mood, and smiled and talked with the rest.

Laura found herself watching his mouth. Oh, that mouth…firm, controlled, yet it could warm into passion and sensuality, spark off a longing and a wild hunger… He turned his dark head and looked at her and, as though he could read her thoughts, colour came into her pale cheeks.

Lifting his glass, his eyes mocking, he said, 'A toast to my blushing bride.'

Echoing, 'To the bride,' everyone followed suit, Maurice and Julian, the two drivers, taking care not to drink too much.

A single-tier wedding-cake was cut, more toasts made, then Tane shot back his immaculate white cuff and, glancing at the slim gold watch strapped to his muscular wrist, remarked, 'We ought to be making a move.'

They were going back to Paris for their honeymoon. A luxury *appartement* on Rue Robiac had been rented and their luggage sent in advance. Before she got into the car, Laura handed her bouquet to Molly, who unexpectedly blushed like a girl. Realising they were momentarily out of earshot of the others, Laura said conspiratorially, 'Maurice seems very... shall we say, *interested*? And he's so *nice*. I know it's a bit soon, but...'

Smiling, Molly quoted Marlowe. '"Who ever loved that loved not at first sight?"'

The newly-weds were driven to the airport, and waved off by the entire party with much gaiety and mirth. Only after they'd left the terminal and boarded the plane did a taut silence descend. During the short flight they scarcely spoke, and when they did they could have been people meeting for the first time, people who could find nothing in common.

When they reached the centre of Paris, and Tane suggested having a night on the town, Laura agreed with alacrity. Anything was better than having to go straight to the *appartement*.

Their garrulous taxi-driver took them to La Chatte Grise, reckoned to be one of the best nightclubs in the city. It proved to be a terrible evening, however. Laura ate food she didn't want, and drank champagne she wanted even less. Smiling until her face felt stiff, she applauded the singer, a French waif with short black hair, huge eyes and a hoarse, haunting voice, and tried to look as if she was enjoying herself. All the time she was aware that Tane was growing steadily more morose.

Eventually, unable to stand any more, she tentatively suggested that they might leave.

He looked momentarily surprised, then said, 'Certainly, if you've had enough.'

After the over-heated atmosphere of the club, the night air was cool and pleasant. The autumn sky was a clear dark blue, sequinned with stars. A glowing moon which looked as if it had been devised for a Hollywood film set hung low over the roof-tops.

'Would you like to walk?' he suggested. 'It's not too far.'

'Yes, that would be nice.'

She had hoped Tane would take her hand, but he didn't. Without speaking they headed towards the Seine. The Parisian streets were bright with lights and thronging with traffic, the broad pavements crowded with pedestrians. For most people the night was just starting.

Rue Robiac, though in the heart of the city, was unspoiled and secluded, its tree-lined pavements shady by day and peaceful by night. The old-style stone *appartement* block was severely grand, with narrow wrought-iron balconies outside long, grey-shuttered windows. It was built in a square with a central courtyard.

They walked through an archway into the moon-drenched court, which was paved with large, well-worn slabs and had a square stone fountain, now dry and dusty, in the centre.

Lights gleamed in several unshuttered windows, and above the doors at each of the four entrances to the building lanterns glowed. Walking a little ahead of her, Tane led the way through a heavy, black-studded door into the main vestibule, elegantly simple with its statues and potted palms and a graceful marble staircase curving up to the next floor.

Having collected the key from the *concierge*, he unlocked a door to their right, and ushered her into a ground-floor *appartement*.

The living-room was charming, furnished with style and comfort in a pleasing blend of colours and textures.

On its polished parquet floor was a beautiful Kashmir carpet in muted shades of green and pink.

There were two bedrooms, with a bathroom between them. Peering in, she noticed with a sense of shock that Tane's luggage had been put in the larger of the two, clearly the master bedroom, while hers was in the other. Both beds had been made up, presumably on Tane's instructions.

When he'd taken off his jacket and thrown it over the back of a chair, he walked to a well-stocked bar and asked, 'Would you like a nightcap?'

Laura shook her head, and watched while he poured himself a brandy.

He glanced at her with irritation and, his voice curt, said, 'I suggest you get into bed.'

She blinked as if he'd struck her. It seemed he *didn't* want her any more, yet there was a tension in him that she sensed was sexual. Resolving to end the uncertainty that was tearing her apart, she drew a deep breath and asked, 'Which bed?'

Tane glanced at her sharply. 'Aren't you afraid I might say mine?'

'No.'

'My, my,' he murmured admiringly. 'You said that as if you meant it, but I'm afraid I'm not in the mood to cope with an unwilling or even a *dutiful* bride.'

'I'm neither one of those.'

Something flared in his eyes, then, a shutter coming down, he said deliberately, 'After your previous stinging rejection, you'd need to convince me of that.'

So that was why he'd made no attempt to touch her. His pride trampled on, he'd made up his mind that the next move must come from *her*.

Laura saw the cynical twist to his lips as she turned to go into the bedroom that held her cases. As the door closed behind her, giving herself no time to think, to change her mind, she stripped off her clothes. When she was totally naked, apart from the string of pearls which gleamed softly against her throat, she caught sight of herself in the cheval-glass, and hesitated.

Though when dressed she appeared to be *very* slim, she was full-busted and her hips curved voluptuously from a slender waist. Her flawless skin was like honey, toning to a pale cream where the sun hadn't touched it.

Since she'd been eating a better diet her face had filled out a little, but now it looked pale, pinched with anxiety, and her beautiful blue eyes had mauve shadows beneath them.

She was running a terrible risk, she knew. Giving Tane the perfect opportunity to hurt and humiliate her, either by taking her roughly, or totally rejecting her. But to put herself voluntarily in this position was the best way she could think of to convince him.

When she opened the door he was standing where she'd left him, head bent, staring into his untasted drink, his dark profile bleak as winter. The click of the latch made him turn.

'Well, well, well...' he murmured. But, instead of coming to take her in his arms, as she'd hoped, he stayed where he was, looking her over with the insolent appraisal of a buyer at a slave market.

Standing framed in the doorway, Laura kept her head high in spite of the burning flush that suffused her face and neck. His leisurely inspection completed, he said softly, 'Come here, Laura.'

Fighting down a cowardly urge to turn tail and run, she went to him. When she was barefooted he seemed to tower over her, making her feel even more nervous and vulnerable.

'If I take you into my bed tonight, that's where you'll stay. There'll be no more rejections, no changing your mind.'

'I wasn't thinking of changing my mind,' she informed him. Then, with an unconscious touch of hauteur, 'I'm your wife now.'

'And you think a wife's place is by her husband's side?'

Despite the blatant mockery in his smoky eyes, she answered seriously, 'Yes, I do.'

An odd note in his voice, he asked, 'Tell me something. Why did you marry me, Laura?'

'You know why.' When he appeared to be still waiting, she added, 'Because you forced me into it.'

'Yes, I did, didn't I?' He tossed back his drink, and put his glass down with a little bang. 'I forced you to marry me, but I can't force you to love me.'

'No one can force another person to love them,' she said sadly, knowing it was only too true.

'Well, come along, wife who doesn't love me, and give me all you have to give.' He bent and swept her into his arms. She was only too thankful that he hadn't walked away and left her to follow him.

Instead of putting her down on the bed as she'd expected, he set her on her feet and looked at her, his eyes like drifting wood-smoke. Smiling a cruel little smile, he said, 'You took off your own clothes willingly enough, suppose you take off mine?'

'T-Tane,' she faltered, no longer sure if she was doing the right thing, 'do you really want me?'

He laughed harshly. 'Surely you've no need to ask a question like that? Oh, yes; I want you.' Taking her hand, he pressed it against his hard body. 'Feel how much I want you.'

But she'd meant so much *more* than just physically. Still, it was *something*.

When he lifted his hand, instead of snatching hers away, as he'd clearly expected, she surprised him by moving it in a light, stroking motion. The jerk of his response gave her a heady feeling of power.

Throwing caution to the winds, she began to undo his shirt buttons, fumbling a trifle as she tugged the silky white material out of his waistband and eased it from his shoulders. Then her fingers found and dealt with the clip of his trousers and the zip.

When he was standing before her, naked and virile, she felt a dryness, a constriction, in her throat, a suffocating excitement that coloured her cheeks and quickened her breathing.

His skin was smooth and deeply tanned, and the sprinkle of dark curly hair that crept down in a V from his broad, muscular chest crisp beneath her touch. His scent—a combination of tangy shower-gel, fresh perspiration, and masculine arousal—was a potent aphrodisiac.

Laura felt no false modesty, no shame, just a sense of utter *rightness*. This was her loved one, her husband, the only man in the world for her. Throwing aside the last of her inhibitions, she went down on her knees and, her hands spread across his buttocks, began to cover his flat stomach with soft butterfly kisses, working her way downwards.

Tane made a sound partway between a gasp and a groan, and, lifting her with strong arms, laid her on the bed and knelt beside her. He looked down into her face, his eyes gleaming between thick, dark lashes. 'What a thoroughly abandoned woman you are. Do you know what happens to abandoned women like you?'

'No,' she whispered breathlessly. 'Tell me, what does happen to them?'

He pinned her beneath him and traced the whorls of her ear with his tongue-tip. 'They end up begging for mercy.'

Recklessly, she said, 'It isn't mercy I'm begging for.'

'By the time I'm through with you, you will be,' he told her.

She lay hot and blissfully helpless in his grip as he thrust hard and deep, filling her with wave after wave of spiralling sensation. Like a man possessed, or a man who feared he might lose what was now his, he made love to her until a munificent morning was spilling its golden sunshine into the room.

Over the succeeding days and nights, Laura gave everything she had to give, complete surrender, total abandonment. But even in their most rapturous moments she was aware that a shadow hung between them.

The weather was wonderful. Kind fortune put on its magician's hat and conjured up an Indian summer of long, calm days, with liquid sunlight golden as honey.

Sun ricocheted from the gold-painted statues on the Pont Alexandre III, while autumn confetti, red and yellow, bronze and russet, fluttered gently down from the gilded trees. Variegated leaves lay in colourful drifts by the Seine, and reflections of the sky made the water look blue.

The nights, clear and star-spangled and romantic, seemed to have been designed especially for lovers.

The thought made Laura's heart ache.

Tane and she were lovers, but only in the most basic, sexual sense. He never held her hand or smiled into her eyes, never cuddled or teased her or sat her on his knee, as he'd once done. There was heat and passion in plenty, but no *warmth*, no *affection*, and it was that which she craved.

Walking endlessly, they made the most of their days, finding fountains playing in hidden squares and marvellous architecture in secret backwaters, climbing flights of steps to sky-window views over the roof-tops, and descending into subterranean gardens, seeing that lovely, intricate city, as only someone on foot could.

They picnicked in the Bois de Boulogne, strolled through the gardens at Versailles, went up the Eiffel Tower, took trips to Fontainebleau, Lisieux, and Chantilly, visited châteaux and museums, the Catacombs and the flea market.

At night they went dancing and dining, to the theatre, the Opera, to shows and nightclubs, and, while it was still running, took more than one trip on the *bateau-mouche*.

The *concierge's* wife, Françoise, a rotund, cheerful little woman, despite her *oignons*, came in daily to keep the *appartement* clean; she also did any shopping that was necessary.

Laura enjoyed cooking, and, for the nights they stayed at home, planned elaborate meals, which were quite often abandoned when Tane had something more important than food on his mind.

One day, towards the end of their month-long honeymoon, a day that had turned cool and grey, with racks of purple clouds gathering low on the horizon and promising rain, they were strolling by the Seine, when they passed a wedding party.

The young couple, blissfully disregarding the weather, were holding hands, the groom looking absurdly proud, the bride smiling and radiant.

Her voice unconsciously holding an undertone of wistfulness, Laura observed, 'Don't they look happy?'

'Why shouldn't they be happy?' Tane demanded with a sudden bitterness that shocked her. 'No doubt they love each other.'

By the time they returned to their *appartement*, the rain had begun in earnest. Laura was feeling tired and unutterably depressed, and her face ached with the effort of holding back the tears that threatened.

Tane went over to the bar and poured an aperitif for them both before asking, 'Where would you like to go this evening? Do you fancy eating at Dominic's?'

'No, I . . . I'm not bothered about going out.'

Though she didn't want it, she accepted the glass of dry sherry he offered her, then sat staring blindly into the pale amber liquid. After a minute or so desperation gave her the courage to ask, 'Tane, what's the matter? What's gone wrong between us?'

'I don't fancy holding an inquest before our honeymoon's even over,' he dismissed brusquely.

'I think we need to,' she persisted. 'Something's wrong. Terribly wrong. And I want to know what it is.'

He stood grim and silent, and she wondered how best to break down the barriers that he'd thrown up between them. Putting the glass of sherry on the table untasted, she made up her mind to try a long shot. 'When Beatrice told you the truth about your parents, why did you say it was no longer relevant?'

At first she thought he wasn't going to answer, then flatly he said, 'Because it *wasn't*. When I told you about my childhood, I still believed I'd driven my parents apart.

But, after you'd said so passionately that no child could break up a marriage unless there was something basically wrong, instead of just blindly accepting the blame I began to bring some intelligence to bear.

'I soon came to the conclusion that you were probably right, and I realised that what my parents had been, or done, no longer mattered. What did matter was the effect I'd allowed it to have on my own life.

'When we split up the first time, perhaps because I already carried such a weight of guilt that I couldn't bear any more, I convinced myself it was all your fault. I told myself it had ended because you hadn't loved me enough, that if you'd really loved me you couldn't have walked out like that...

'Then after a while I began to see that it was my own fear and insecurity that had driven you away. You'd said so bluntly that children were part of a marriage, and the more I turned your words over in my mind, the more I realised you were right.

'My thinking had been warped and twisted. Your wish for children was happy and normal, whereas I'd been mentally breeding chimeras.

'I started to watch families sharing things, having fun together. Soon I began to wonder what it would be like to have a child of my own to love—a child who would call me "Daddy" and love me back. I saw myself holding its hand to stop it falling, teaching it things...

'When Christmas Eve came I pictured our children tucked up in bed, and the two of us decorating the tree and laughing together while we filled stockings. Then me playing Santa Claus while you waited by the fire...'

Laura sat with her eyes fast on his face, tears trickling unheeded down her cheeks and dripping into her lap.

'I imagined myself building a doll's house, helping to set up a train set, playing football with my son, taking my daughter to ballet classes...

'I knew that, if I could only find you and persuade you to give me another chance, I'd be prepared to have as many children as you wanted. So long as you were happy, I'd be happy too.'

Laura wiped her face with her fingers, and, when she could find her voice, whispered, 'So if it isn't that—if you don't mind about Jamie, about being his father——'

'Of course I don't mind!' Tane sounded almost fierce. 'I was bitterly jealous when I thought he was Belmont's. If you had a child, I wanted more than anything for him to be *mine*.'

'But when you asked me to marry you, you said you didn't want Jamie. Was that because you then thought he was David's?'

'No.' Tane looked almost shamefaced. 'I was testing your feelings for me. Isn't it ludicrous—a grown man being jealous of a child?' He gave a bitter little laugh. 'But just for once I wanted to feel I came *first*.

'If you'd agreed to marry me, I would have been only too pleased to accept Jamie as my own. But you said you wouldn't marry me in any circumstances...'

Laura gripped her hands together tightly, fingers entwined. 'But now we *are* married, and still there's something...not right.'

'Oh, yes, we're married, but what's not right is that I've had to force you every step of the way. You recall what you said: "Isn't a forced marriage just storing up heartache and misery for both of us?"'

'But *you* said it was better than no marriage at all.'

'I was mistaken.'

She looked up at him, the last vestige of colour draining from her face. 'Mistaken?'

He rubbed a hand across the back of his neck. 'When I first saw you again I think I went a little mad. You looked at me so coolly, and I knew you felt nothing for me. All my bitterness and anger came flooding back. I'd had four years of heartache and you'd got off scot-free. I made up my mind to have you back, to make you pay.

'But then, when we talked, I realised that I hadn't been the only one to suffer. I still wanted you back, though now my goal was different. I wanted to marry you and make you happy. I told myself that once you were mine I'd somehow *make* you love me, *make* our marriage work.

'Now, after these last weeks, I'm forced to admit I've failed. It isn't working.'

'It *is* working,' she protested. 'We've been...' balking at the word 'happy', she substituted '...content, haven't we?'

'On the surface, maybe. But you know as well as I do that we can't go on this way.'

Her heart beating in slow, heavy thuds, Laura waited like a victim on the steps of the guillotine.

Tane sat down opposite and, as if unutterably weary, rested his dark, shapely head against the back of the chair. 'I accept that the blame is entirely mine. I've treated you abominably all along the line.

'When I found you again, despite everything, I still hadn't learnt any sense. I poured out all my own pain and desolation without ever thinking of yours.' His face bleak, introspective, he went on, 'Then, when we became lovers once more, I was still way out of line, arrogant and selfish enough to think only of myself, to demand a lot more than I had any right to ask.

'If you ever did feel any love for me, as you say you did, I killed it. All that was left was a powerful sexual attraction.'

Ignoring Laura's attempt to interrupt, with a thickness in his usually clear voice, he continued, 'The first time I destroyed what we had by letting a childhood bogy come between us, this time I ruined what we might have had by using strong-arm tactics. But I was desperate, terrified of losing you again. I *had* to keep some hold over you. Only I've realised, somewhat belatedly, that it doesn't work.

'That night, after I'd forced you to agree to marry me, I waited, hoping against hope that, though you were understandably angry and resentful, you'd show some sign of forgiveness, some indication that you were glad to be with me again. But you didn't. You wouldn't even kiss me. When you turned away, I saw red.'

He groaned. 'Dear God, you'll never know how I felt when you said so quietly, "I don't want to look at you. I never want to see you again. I hate you."

'If I'd had an ounce of compassion I'd have walked out of your life there and then. But, even though you'd admitted you hated me, I still couldn't bear the thought of never seeing you again...'

While he'd been talking, Laura had got to her feet. Now she stood white-faced and tense, habit making her tug at the gold chain which, after her wedding day, she'd gone back to wearing.

All at once Tane jumped to his feet and, with a savage oath, grasped the chain and jerked at it, snapping the thin links. As Laura gave a startled cry, he threw it across the room with frightening violence.

It skittered across the wood-block floor and disappeared beneath a polished sideboard.

Overwrought, Laura burst into tears and, running across the room, went down on her knees to scrabble beneath the heavy piece of furniture. Strong hands seized her shoulders and hauled her to her feet.

She fought to free herself, sobbing, 'Leave me alone...leave me *alone*, damn you! I want to find it.'

Tane crushed her against him, stilling her struggles, pressing her head against his broad expanse of chest.

'Oh, God...I'm sorry...I'm sorry. It's my rotten temper. Don't cry.'

But she was unable to stop, all the worry, the uncertainty, the hopes and fears, the pent-up unhappiness of the last few weeks finding an outlet.

He groaned. 'Hush, now; I know what it means to you. I'll find it, I promise.' But still she wept, with an abandonment that proved just what a strain she'd been under.

When finally she'd cried herself out, and was drawing long, shuddering breaths, he led her to a chair and gently pushed her into it.

Crouching down, he felt under the sideboard. With his long arm he succeeded where she'd failed. In a trice he located the chain and dropped it into her lap.

Almost humbly, he said, 'Forgive me; I'll have it mended.'

She looked up at him then, her face blotched and tear-stained, her eyelids pink and puffy. *'Why?'*

A dark flush ran along his high cheekbones. 'You said it was Belmont's last gift to you. You quite obviously treasure it...it's a constant reminder to me that you've had a husband. A husband you still love. A living man I might have coped with, but how do I fight a ghost, a saint, a martyr?

'I wanted to be the only man in the world for you.'
He laughed harshly. 'How selfish, how self-centred, how
bloody egotistical! But there it is. As I said before, I'm
not quite sane where you're concerned.'

She started to shake her head. 'Tane, I——'

Bitterly he demanded, 'Surely it's not sane to be
jealous of a dead man?'

The idea of Tane being jealous wasn't a new one. What
was new was discovering the *depth* of that jealousy, the
way it was gnawing at him, eating away at his self-
control.

He'd said, 'It's my rotten temper.' But in the past he'd
always been good-tempered, and well able to keep his
feelings in check. She closed her eyes briefly. Hadn't she
feared that they might end up destroying one another?

Gathering all her reserves of strength, she said steadily,
'There's no need to be jealous of David.'

His mouth twisted wryly. 'I overheard you tell Aunt
Beatrice what a wonderful person he was, and how you
still loved him. Are you denying that now, saying it isn't
the truth?'

'No.' She refused to deny it. 'I do love him. I always
will, but——'

'I should never have forced you to go through with
the wedding!' Tane burst out. 'I was getting your delectable body, but a dead man kept your love. I knew
at the time it would never work, yet I couldn't bring
myself to give you up, to face an empty future.' He made
a gesture of defeat. 'But now I've accepted the fact that
I must let you go.'

'"Let me go"?' she echoed stupidly. 'I don't understand what you mean by "let me go".'

'Allow you to leave me, to live your own life.' His
voice was quietly implacable. 'I'll buy a house for you

and make you an allowance. You won't have to work unless you want to.'

She swallowed. 'What about Jamie?'

'I'll take care of his education. Everything he needs.'

'He needs a father.'

'With your permission, I'll visit him.'

Oh, where was the old, arrogant Tane? She couldn't bear to see him humble, defeated. Levelly she said, 'I mean a full-time father.'

Pain in his blue-grey eyes, Tane said, 'I'll give you grounds for a divorce, then if you ever want to marry again——'

'I would never marry just for Jamie's sake.'

'You might meet someone...' He paused, then went on with a hint of desperation, 'You're not the kind of woman who should live alone. You need a husband, more children to make a real family...'

Laura lifted her chin and spoke clearly. 'I don't want a husband unless it's *you*. I don't want any more children unless they're *yours*.'

Just for a moment his eyes blazed, then he said with something close to anguish, 'I can't take it.' Sinking into the nearest chair, he dropped his dark head in his hands. 'I once told you I wanted *everything*, and that was the simple truth, but in the end the only thing that really matters is having your love.'

He spoke heavily, his voice hoarse. 'All my life I've lived without love, and I can go on doing it. What I *can't* do is live with a woman whose heart is given to a dead man.'

Laura got out of her chair and knelt by his side. 'If you'd come back a little sooner that day at the hospital, you'd have heard me tell Beatrice that I love *you*. That I *always* loved you.

'God knows, I bitterly regret the years we've wasted, but I can't regret what small pleasure they gave David.'

Her voice very low, she went on, 'You've no need to be jealous. I loved David, I always will, but I loved him as a brother.'

'If he'd been your brother, that would be different, but he wasn't, he was your *husband*.'

'But he *wasn't*, at least not in the full sense of the word. He gave me his name and looked after Jamie and me as well as he could, but he treated me as a sister.'

Tane lifted her face to his with an urgent hand. 'Do you mean you *never* shared his bed?'

'I never slept with him. I couldn't have done, no matter how much he wanted me. But, when he realised how utterly and completely I was yours, he never pressed me to. It was taken for granted that we'd have separate rooms.'

Still she had to be totally honest. 'The last few weeks before he was forced to go into hospital he was very weak, and often he couldn't settle at night because of the pain. I'd hear him moving about restlessly, and then I'd go and lie beside him and hold him until he fell asleep in my arms.'

Gruffly, Tane said, 'I couldn't begrudge the poor devil that comfort.'

Taking his hand, Laura held it against her cheek. 'You are the only man I've loved completely. The only man I've ever slept with. Don't end our marriage. I need you, Jamie needs you.' She looked into his dark face. 'If you can't love me, I'll try not to let it make any difference.'

'I'm afraid that won't do.'

She drew away, cold with despair.

He took her upper arms in a grip that hurt, and shook her slightly. 'If we stay together I want it to make *all* the difference. I want you to need my love as much as I need yours. I want both to give and receive a lifetime's commitment.'

'Oh, Tane...' It was the 'amen' to a prayer. She turned her face into his neck with a wave of love that broke over them both and swamped them, leaving them clinging together like castaways.

After a while she stirred and looked into the eyes of this man who had set his mark on her soul. 'I'm yours, now and forever.'

'And I'm yours.' Tane's response was a solemn affirmation. Running his fingers into her silky hair, he held her head between his hands and kissed her passionately. Then, thumbs caressing her cheeks, he suggested, 'Come to bed; you look tired.'

Her dimples appeared as she chuckled and said huskily, 'Not too tired.'

Some time later, lying warm and drowsy in his arms, naked flesh to naked flesh, she sighed contentedly. He still hadn't said in so many words that he cared for her, still hadn't *called* her his love. But she knew she *was*, and she was satisfied. Though it would be wonderful to hear it, she thought wistfully.

Listening to the autumn rain beating against the tall windows, she kissed the smooth skin of his shoulder and remarked, 'It's a pity our honeymoon is nearly over. All these weeks I've wanted to kiss you, to sit on your lap, and be petted and cuddled; I've wanted us to hold hands in the street, to smile at each other and be as foolishly, blatantly in love as the other honeymoon couple we saw.'

'That's for me,' Tane agreed instantly. His arms tightened. 'Instead of waiting years, we'll have our second honeymoon straight away. Would you like to stay on in

Paris, or shall we go somewhere warmer, more exotic, where it's not likely to rain?'

Cuddling closer, Laura put into words what she'd once thought. 'I don't mind a cold, wet month in West Hartlepool, so long as you're there with me.'

She was amply rewarded.

'My own, my dearest love,' he said deeply, and kissed her.

HARLEQUIN®

PRESENTS *Plus*

"Virgin or wanton?" Oliver Lee is suspicious of everything and everyone.... When he meets Fliss, he thinks her innocence is an act. Fliss *may* be innocent, but the passion Oliver inspires in her is just like raw silk—beautiful, unique and desirable. But like raw silk it is fragile....Only love will help it survive.

Ben Claremont seemed to be the only man in the world who didn't lust after Honey's body...but he asked her to marry him anyway! Honey wasn't in love with him—so separate rooms would suit her just fine! But what on earth had she gotten herself into? Were their wedding vows based on a lie?

Presents Plus—the Power of Passion!

Coming next month:

Raw Silk by Anne Mather
Harlequin Presents Plus #1731

and

Separate Rooms by Diana Hamilton
Harlequin Presents Plus #1732

Harlequin Presents Plus
The best has just gotten better!

Available in April wherever Harlequin books are sold.